The majority of the proceeds from the book will support research on
pregnant or parenting mothers and infants/children prenatally
exposed to substances.

Dedication

This book is dedicated to the mothers who shared
their stories included in this collection.

Dedicated to the families of the authors
for their support and encouragement.

Acknowledgments

Book Cover is Original Artwork © by Mary Louise Wilson
Formatting by Robert Atkinson
Editing support by Cherry Odem
Research supported by a Classroom Award Atlas.ti
Student participation supported by Clemson University
Creative Inquiry Program

CLEMSON
School of NURSING

Mary Ellen Wright, PhD, APRN, CPNP-PC

Dr. Mary Ellen Wright is currently an Assistant Professor in the School of Nursing at Clemson University, Clemson, South Carolina. Dr. Wright has been a nurse practitioner in the specialties of obstetrics, gynecology and pediatrics since 1981. Her clinical work has been in prenatal and pediatric care of families in the community which included special interests of mothers affected by substance use, adolescent pregnancy, pediatric HIV, child maltreatment, prenatal education, social support for developing families and developmental pediatrics. Dr. Wright's funded research involves social support for vulnerable families, with most recent work focusing on families affected by substance use and families affected by domestic violence. Dr. Wright is on the Board of Directors of the International Association for Human Caring and has been named a great 100 nurse of North Carolina. She presents at international, national and regional conferences that address the health needs of families.

Dr. Wright's reflection on the experience of this project:

As co-principal investigator of this project, I was stirred by an immense sense of appreciation for the mothers who shared their stories. The stories were told from the heart by the mothers and moved our team to tears. I was inspired by the examples of love, caring and resiliency as they face the everyday battle with addiction. I was moved by the collaborators on the study as to their expressions of emotions, reflections and compassion for the mothers who told their stories. Their reflections fostered the hope that others reading these stories will reflect and find new perspectives on people with addiction, especially mothers. I am committed to make the mothers' stories available to as many people as possible, so that the world will respond in a caring and supportive manner that promotes the wellbeing of mothers and children. The majority of the proceeds from the book will support research on mothers, infants and children affected by substance use disorder.

Heide S. Temples, PhD, APRN, PPCNP-BC, IBCLC

Dr. Heide Temples is currently a tenured Associate Professor in the School of Nursing at Clemson University, Clemson, South Carolina where she teaches pediatrics to nurse practitioner students. Dr. Temples has been a pediatric nurse practitioner since 1993. Most of her clinical practice has been in underserved, rural and inner city communities serving minority populations. Her life-long interest is providing the tools for parents to raise happy, healthy, and well-adjusted children. Dr. Temples' research includes sharing the mother's experience with drug dependence while raising children, to improve health care services for families. Dr. Temples is also researching the epigenetic influence of human milk in decreasing the risk of developing obesity and type-2-diabetes.

Dr. Temples' reflection on the experience of this project:

As faculty members at Clemson University, Dr. Wright and I provided this research opportunity to the students in our Creative Inquiry Program. Mothers eagerly shared their stories of battling addiction while raising a family. During the anonymous phone interviews, I watch the students transform before my eyes. Upon reflection, the research experience was an awaking for the students and me. We now understand that the mothers did not want this to happen to them or their babies. The mothers were dependent on highly addictive substances when they discovered they were pregnant. They left their families and friends to stay in recovery centers and took daily prescription medication throughout the pregnancy to stay off street drugs that could harm the unborn baby. Through this research, the students learned to actively listen and empathize with the families using care and compassion. Listening to the mother's stories was a life-changing experience for many of our students...as it was for me. It is a gift and privilege to share these stories of addiction and recovery.

Contributing Authors

Olivia Chafe: Olivia is a Biological Sciences major with a Chemistry minor at Clemson University and plans to pursue pediatric clinical pharmacy.

Reflection: This research helped me understand that the stereotypical picture of addiction is not accurate. Many women in our study began their struggles with addiction after receiving a prescription for pain and had no intention of using it long term. What most profoundly affected me during this research experience is how much some of these mothers were motivated by their children to work their programs and get their babies back from family members and foster care placements. It also demonstrated that the effects of addiction are more widespread than I originally believed. Not only is the life of the person struggling with addiction forever changed, but so are the lives of their families. When their family or another social support system aids a person struggling with substance abuse problems there is a strong positive correlation with that person's ability to overcome their addiction. Discovering that correlation allowed me to comprehend the importance of ensuring proper care and support systems for mothers with addiction.

Lauren M. Drum: Lauren is a Nursing Major at Clemson University and plans to pursue graduate education as a Neonatal Nurse Practitioner. In her free time, Lauren serves as a Senator for Clemson's Undergraduate Student Government and is on the Board for Clemson Student Nurses' Association.

Reflection: This research helped me understand that addiction is truly a disease. As a future nurse that wants to work with infants and their mothers, I now have the knowledge to interact with these mothers using the utmost compassion and understanding. The foundation of nursing is rooted in caring for others, and this research has the potential to change the way nurses and other healthcare professionals interact with mothers battling substance abuse.

Kelly Edwards: Kelly is a student in Health Science at Clemson University and plans to pursue a career in occupational therapy.

Reflection: This research provided me with valuable experience in understanding the challenges faced by mothers with addiction, which is a population that is often misunderstood. In being part of this project, I was able to better understand some of the determinants that lead to addiction and the potential improvements that can be made in the healthcare system to meet the needs of those fighting addiction. I also have a different view of the stigmatization of addiction and how harmful stigma can be when it plays a part in healthcare delivery.

Jacob A. Estrada: Jacob is a senior Biological Sciences major at Clemson University, and plans to pursue a career in healthcare and practice medicine.

Reflection: This research helped me to not generalize as much when looking at a person. I understand the term addiction so much more now than I did prior to taking part in this program. Now, I know to look at the person instead of the word and it helps tremendously when I think about **how each of them has their own story to tell behind their life events. I learned in detail about** the relationships within families and friend networks, and how much those impact decisions, like how a family can push and pull you out of addiction like you're on a theme park ride with seemingly no control. I want to take what I've learned about addiction and never forget it, because it happens everywhere, all the time, and the more people who understand it, the better chance we have of reaching out and finding help for those in need, the better chance we have of conquering it.

Emily Guthrie: Emily is a Genetics major at Clemson University and looks forward to pursuing a medical degree after graduation to explore her interest in Neonatology.

Reflection: The research helped me understand that addiction is an illness. Every woman has their own story and unique circumstances that have marked their lives. More importantly, I have learned about the obstacles many of these women face while on their paths to recovery. This has taught me to always have an open-mind and be constantly uplifting and supportive of anyone facing similar situations. Often, this world can be judgmental or assume stigmas about those going through drug addiction and recovery. I have learned so much from the women who tell their stories in this book, especially when it comes to how we can create better support systems in our communities.

Erin Hatcher: Erin is a Nursing major at Clemson University and plans to pursue graduate education as a Nurse Anesthetist.

Reflection: This research helped me to better understand the experiences of mothers who have struggled with drug use while raising children. It was so humbling to be able to interview and hear the personal stories of the study participants. The common themes we found when analyzing the interviews opened my eyes to different struggles the mothers faced, and showed me ways to be a better nurse in the future.

Colton Hunter: Colton is a junior Health Science major with a concentration in Pre-Professional Health Studies and a minor in Spanish Studies. He is originally from Belton, SC, so attending Clemson University has always been a lifelong goal of his. After graduating from Clemson, he hopes to attend medical school in the pursuit of a career in pediatric surgery with an emphasis in low income and Spanish-speaking populations. After receiving an MD, he would love to move to a Spanish-speaking country to work with Doctors Without Borders for an extended period of time.

Reflection: Both the Spanish language and working with children are huge passions of mine, which is one of the reasons I chose to participate in the Perinatal Substance Exposure Creative Inquiry. I have learned a lot of valuable information through our research, and I plan to apply this knowledge in the future as a practicing physician.

Elizabeth Johnson: Elizabeth is a Biochemistry and Genetics double major at Clemson University and plans to pursue a career as a Nurse Practitioner with an emphasis in epidemiology.

Reflection: This research provided a unique perspective into the mind of mothers who are dependent on opioids and other illicit substances. Prior to this endeavor, I had little exposure to this particular topic, and it has been enlightening to have this opportunity to study it. Through these very personal narratives of mothers, their story is made known, and hopefully their thoughts and experiences can be implemented into providing better treatments for those recovering from similar dependencies. This research completely eliminated any previously held notions regarding the stigma surrounding dependency to reveal a more empathetic approach to engaging with any individual struggling with dependency.

Rebekah Lannamann: Rebekah is a sophomore Nursing major from Spartanburg, South Carolina. She chose to participate in this research because she is interested in pursuing a future in Neonatal Nursing.

Reflection: Before beginning our research, I was under the assumption that strict and restrictive policies were the most beneficial way to provide a means for recovery. After conducting the qualitative research and speaking to the mothers, it was revealed to me that through positive support, care, and compassion-especially accompanied by their baby, the mothers are much more likely to fully recover from their addictions. Through the use of the ATLAS.ti software tool, we were able to assess themes that were across different stories. It was interesting how correlations were seen amongst many of the mothers, thus contributing to our findings.

Carla M. Lautenschlager: Carla is a Biological Sciences major and Spanish Studies minor at Clemson University who plans to pursue medical school to help underserved populations.

Reflection: This research, and the book that it produced, are my greatest accomplishments. The opioid epidemic is a grave issue in this country, and I am passionate about bringing awareness to its severity and also ending the stigma surrounding the issue. Because I am so passionate about the issue, after listening to these mother's stories I feel as though I am their biggest supporters. I am certain when this book is published, it will not only inform the public about the issue, but also bring light to what is really going on in these circumstances. Through this experience, I have learned so much about compassion, listening, and communicating with individuals about difficult situations. My favorite part of this Creative Inquiry was seeing the impact of this research on health care and learning from the participants that were interviewed.

Haley McKee: Haley McKee is a Nursing major and Spanish Language minor at Clemson University with a Certificate in Global Health. She plans pursue pediatric Nursing after graduation.

Reflection: This research has helped me to understand the multi-faceted stories behind individuals' struggles in a way that I did not before. It also helped me to understand the strength of maternal love for children and the power of positive and negative social influences in all peoples' lives. After hearing these stories and noticing the common themes of social influences that either drove mothers toward harmful coping behaviors or motivated them to fight the disease of addiction, I started to realize how social support could be instrumental in helping us to help women who are struggling.

Daniel S. Rafalski
Daniel graduated from Clemson University with a degree in Biology and plans to pursue a career as an OB/GYN.

Reflection: This research has helped me understand the struggles of addiction, especially from the standpoint of mothers. I also have come to better acknowledge that those facing addiction need to be looked at with open arms rather than shut down and shunned, as many in today's world have. I also learned, although, as a man I don't think I will ever truly understand, that becoming a mother is one of the most, or can be one of the most, powerful periods in a woman's life. The attachment a mother has with her child can be insurmountable, and after participating in this research, I learned that this connection between a mother and child should be utilized in recovering mothers as it is one of the biggest motivational forces.

Jennifer C. Rumsey: Jennifer is a Microbiology/Biomedicine major at Clemson University and plans to pursue medical school after graduation.

Reflection: This research helped me see that addiction truly is a disease. I learned so much about the complexities and hardships associated with addiction, as well as the lack of resources to seek help. This research taught me so much and gave me a deeper understanding of how detrimental addiction can be to a family.

Emily Y. Shores: Emily Shores is a Health Science major at Clemson University with a dual minor in Genetics and Biological Sciences. She intends to pursue medical school after graduation.

Reflection: This project has opened my eyes to the importance of both maternal and child health care- that one cannot exist without the other. Providers cannot handle only the infants, they must also understand the mother. This project has brought to my attention how little research there is in the area of perinatal substance exposure and the importance of understanding what a drug-addicted mother goes through. As a nation, we have a long way to go regarding stigma and statistics in this field, but I see great hope starting with this project. These mothers are still mothers, and their addiction does not deprive them of that title.

Brooks Woody: Brooks is a Health Science major with a double concentration in Pre-Professional Health Studies and Health Promotion and Behavior and a minor in Psychology at Clemson University. She plans to pursue a career in Health Promotion working specifically with children.

Reflection: This research helped me understand the mother's perspective of Neonatal Abstinence Syndrome. Often times in our society we jump to conclusions and judge others based on what we think is right, rather than listening to what other people have to say. You also never know exactly what someone has been through, and therefore I believe there is a lack of empathy in our society, which is important in order to be a good human. We need to broaden our views and resources for addicts to better assist them in treatment and recovery, because they are people too. Addiction is not a moral defect, but rather a mental illness, and their life is just as important and precious as yours.

Molly Yost: Molly is a Nursing student at Clemson University and plans to specialize in Neonatal Nursing.

Reflection: This research expanded my scope on patients' potential circumstances. It instilled in me a great respect for every person I come across as everybody has their own battles. I have become very passionate about changing the stigma of mothers facing addiction and hope that one day we can change it entirely. It has also given me the knowledge and ability to ask myself questions about other situations I may have misjudged and how I can correct those to help other people.

"I Do Love My Baby"
Stories of Mothers with Substance Addiction and Recovery

Introduction

Just saying the word "addiction" for each of us brings a different picture of the people affected. The description of someone with active addiction, or seeking recovery, often includes terms of judgement and stigma. Mothers with addiction are particularly vulnerable to being stigmatized. Understandably, the safety of the child or children remains the priority when a family is affected by addiction. However, the response of society should include the promotion of recovery and support for the mother with addiction.

A caring response to the situation of a family affected by addiction requires coming to know the mother, family members and children. The stories in this book were voluntarily told by mothers who have the chronic disease of addiction and are in various phases of recovery. Each mother stated her desire to share her story was driven by the hope that her words will affect society's tendency to judge and stigmatize mothers with addiction. The book also includes a story from a grandmother and a story from a kinship foster mother who is caring for child placed with her by child protective services.

The basic premise of the book is that all people are caring, which is a based on an assumption of the theory of Nursing as Caring (Boykin & Schoenhofer, 1993). We can think of caring in each person like a light dimmer switch. There is always electric current active in the light even if the dimmer switch is turned down. Caring is like the electric current in the light and is always present. Depending on the situation and the supports within and around the person, their caring may show or be dimmed.

As these stories are read, the question is: Are you someone who pushes the dimmer switch up for people to let their light shine bright or are you someone who pushes the light switch down dimming the other person's light? If you met a mother with addiction, would you judge her and say unkind words to her, or would you give her supportive words and actions that would encourage her and bring forth caring? Can you imagine yourself being an advocate to change the attitudes of judgement and stigma for persons with addiction?

In the stories there are many themes that include trauma as children, abusive treatment, unhealthy relationships, as well as stories of positive support, love, hope, perseverance, and caring. At the end of each chapter are reflections for the readers to consider that are connected to the story.

At the end of the book is a list of international and national resources for families with addiction or citizens of the world to learn more about addiction and recovery.

Thank you for taking this journey of discovery and reflection on the topic of mothers with addiction and recovery. You may feel a variety of emotions reading the stories. I hope that by reading the stories you will embark on your own journey of reflection on your beliefs and attitudes regarding addiction.

Mary Ellen Wright

CHAPTER 1

Hoping for Love

Story retold by Colton Hunter, Brooks Woody, Mary Ellen Wright

The story of hope, love and resiliency told by a grandmother about her own alcoholism, her daughter's addiction to drugs and the effect on the family.

Where I Come From

I was the youngest child in my family, but I felt that my other siblings were more favored by my parents. I was different from the other children. I thought of myself as strange. I looked different, acted independent as a free thinker and didn't conform to my family's southern, traditional, ideal way of living. I continued to be my own person. I think my way of being probably scared my parents, because they couldn't control me. Instead of celebrating my uniqueness, my family made me feel ashamed.

The disdain my family had for my differences had a huge impact on some of my life decisions. I thought if I ever had more than one child, I would have to pick a favorite. Now, I finally understand that favoring one child over another doesn't have to be part of motherhood.

Following My Own Dreams

I was raised Catholic, went to an all Catholic girls' school, and an all Catholic girls' college. I knew what I wanted to be when I graduated from college, but my father had a different plan in mind. He was a coach and he treated his children like we were his team. He constantly pitted us against each other in competitions. He stated often how incompetent he thought I was to follow my dreams. The phrases still ring in my head of his disapproving statements: 1.) you could never do that; 2.) that's not something you could do, because it's just unreal; 3.) you're not capable of that. These were the messages I was being sent throughout my childhood. I think that it had a profound effect on me.

Into the Rabbit Hole

I was a recreational drug user as a young person and my use escalated quickly. I knew when I was in middle school that I had the addictive gene. I can remember drinking and getting drunk. I believe the gene for addiction in my life got passed down to me. As I began high school, recreational drug use was part of my life and continued through college. I didn't really think a whole lot about it at the time, because it didn't seem to impact me in derogatory ways.

I completed school and had a job that I never lost. In my mind, I was functioning even when using recreationally.

Relationship Effect

As I became older the impact of drug use affected my personal relationships. Drug use destroyed my ability to be in a quality relationship. Of course, I fell in love with a man that was a user as well. I thought when we got married, we would live happily ever after, like a fairy tale. The addiction would magically disappear. Well, we all know where that leads us. So, I married this guy who was an addict.

I got pregnant a year after I married him. I had my daughter, and I thought I would kick into this traditional life of being a mom. But my husband's addictions got worse and worse. His addictions were much deeper than I had ever really imagined. He was a sex addict, as well. I kept thinking that I could change this man, but it didn't work out that way. There was a lot of trauma and a lot of missed opportunities on my behalf. I was co-dependent, and my addiction really hindered my ability to function or to reach out for help in a healthy way.

The worst effect ended up landing on my daughter. She witnessed a lot of dysfunctional anger and rage. She was affected by the fact that I was caught up in the addiction as well. I was still drinking, but addiction can be

2

to any sort of substance that prevents logical decision making.

Traumatic Event

In the middle of my daughter's adolescence, her dad was diagnosed with AIDS and also had a stroke. At that time, HIV was considered the plague, which made it much more difficult for us to tell anyone and get the support both my daughter and I needed. As a teenager, my daughter witnessed her father waste away. At that point, I realized maybe I should leave this guy. I still loved this man, and I knew I couldn't leave him while he was dying. I stuck it out with him and gave him a home to live his last days. I was very much in love with him, and I think I still am, even though he is gone now. He passed away two decades ago of AIDS.

The side effect was that my daughter witnessed it all. I was unable to see the impact it would have on her. My daughter was well on her way to an unhealthy life, because she witnessed all these things. I was not able to parent her the way she deserved to be parented.

Just the Two of Us

After my husband passed away, my alcoholism really flared. My family turned away from me. We, my daughter and I, were an act of survival. She was traumatized. I was traumatized. As she grew into her teenage years, she witnessed my alcoholism. I feel very responsible for bringing my addiction into her world. At that time, I was still unable to own my own alcoholism. I kept justifying my drinking. I was numbing out all my pain from my husband. I was numbing out my traumatic childhood.

Next Generation of Drug Use

My daughter, at the ripe old age of legality, moved away from home and began her descent into addiction. Her addictive behaviors were beyond anything I could ever imagine. She was in the generation that used high-tech drugs, like psychedelic drugs. She fell into the abyss of addiction, with the type of people that I never thought, in my whole life, she would have contact. I never imagined having a daughter who was into heavy drugs. I blamed myself. I couldn't save her.

So, at this point, we did the relocation fix. I thought moving away was going to change everything. My daughter moved with me.

Before too much time passed in our new place, my daughter decided to move out and go back to where we used to live. She met a guy. My friends were calling me and saying that she was being beaten up. My friends told me she had black eyes and a broken nose. They told me that I needed to come and get my daughter. They said I needed to come and save her. At this point, I saw the light. They were calling me and telling me she's bad off. I knew she was no longer with me, and I was not happy in the new place I was living, so I decided to leave there. When I returned to protect her, I couldn't find her. I called helplines to report her missing and to find out if she was dead or alive. I didn't know what to do. It was agony.

A Fresh Start

Eventually, I took a weekend off to just take a drive. As I explored different areas, I found a beautiful place to live and pursue a fresh start for me. I returned home and threw my stuff in a truck and moved to this wonderful place. I started going to Alcoholics Anonymous (AA) meetings, thinking that my daughter was the problem, not me.

One night, I was sitting in an open AA meeting and this man told his story about his mother. He described her as an untreated alcoholic. It just hit me like a ton of bricks, that I was that mother. I am an alcoholic. I never thought of myself as one. So, at the end of the meeting the leader of the group invites anyone who wants to live a clean life to come and pick up a white chip. On that night, I don't know how I got up out of my chair, it was like something pushed me up out of it, and I went and picked up a white chip. At that point, I accepted my own addiction and my own dark secret of this traumatic life that I've lived. The universe was telling me to get my shit together and help my daughter.

Years later I discovered that the same day I picked up that white chip and realized my addiction, my daughter had overdosed and was revived. It seems uncanny the very day I accepted my addiction, my daughter nearly died from her addiction. I knew she had a whole lifetime of fear, abuse and neglect from my alcoholism and now I had to make it up to her somehow.

Slowly Picking Up the Pieces

It was a daunting thought to make up for my daughter's whole lifetime. Surprisingly, one day she reached out to me and asked to come to where I was living. When she got off the bus she was accompanied by an abusive boyfriend. She had a black eye and a big belly. She was pregnant. I never thought I would survive all the events that were to follow. I had to watch her being beaten up. When I tried to help, she rejected me. She never was home and sometimes slept on the street pregnant. I went to visit her in the hospital, because her boyfriend beat her up so badly that she had to be hospitalized. Her first son, who is now a teenager, was beaten in utero. When she had him she was not ready to get clean. She didn't want to live with me. One day after the baby was born, I went to visit them at her house. I was shocked, it was a crack house. I didn't know what to do. She asked me if I could go to McDonalds and get her a little carton of milk for the baby. I looked in his bed and it was just filthy dirty and wet. So, I had to call family social services. They took him away from her and this horrible living condition and brought him to me.

At the time, I was working in my dream job. I had to quit, because I had this child needed my care. This little baby boy was another trauma victim. It was just like something you see in a movie, but it's your own life you're living. I never gave up hope on my daughter. I always knew or rather hoped that somewhere, somehow she would return home.

Years go by, as I am raising my grandson, my daughter gets pregnant again. She was in another abusive relationship. This guy is beating her up in front of the baby again. The addiction kept her in these relationships. At this point in her life, she could not survive without drugs. Then her second child was placed by social services to live with me. She didn't lose custody of him though.

She was still with this abusive guy. He would tell her I was bad for her and tell me she didn't want to be with me. He was driving us apart. This went on for almost a decade. She was in rehab a good four or five times throughout these years. I think for some women, addiction to men is probably the worst addiction of all. Those women try to do better, and these guys bring them down again. They see the women as a meal ticket or worse, a way to get drugs.

My daughter got pregnant for a third time. I was beside myself. She would've just been another statistic, but she went to the recovery center. I prayed for her to have a breakthrough, like I had when I picked up the white chip and admitted my addiction. After she had the third child, I think

5

that the psychic change hit her. She has now been clean for a year. The baby's birthday is soon.

Thoughts About Our Journey to Recovery

To watch my beautiful, little child grow up and be beaten by men who viewed her as just an object. It was pain beyond my wildest imagination. I stuck it out with her, but I never lost hope and love for her. We are a family living together. I've adopted her oldest child to help with his special needs. As a teenager, he expresses his anger towards her at times. We continue to revisit the trauma. He is aware of all her bad choices.

My concern now is for my grandchildren's future. Does the pain and trauma go on? Do these children warrant the sickness that we all have? Will we be able to guide them away from those choices that are genetically predisposed in us?

So, that's where we are now. She is a great mother to her youngest two children. Her oldest child reminds her daily of all her mistakes. I think it's just a miracle we are all here and alive. We survived it. That's the story. There is no magic wand. The pain resurfaces from time to time. The gift that we were given, far outweighs the evil that came into our lives. Addiction is a gripping story, but that's our story.

The Takeaway

The attitude of my family growing up was snobby and judgmental. If you didn't have the right credentials, you were not considered good enough to be my friend. I think there is still a part of that in me. We can't judge anyone, it's just people trying the best they can. My daughter taught me that lesson in her life experience, and for that I'm grateful. I'm always reminded by my daughter's beautiful soul.

You know, a lot of people look at addiction like it's a moral defect. There needs to be an insight as to where these young women are who have addiction. All they are looking for is love and acceptance. The thinking of our society and culture could be reshaped in understanding that taking drugs is not a moral defect, but a combination of situation and genetics. People need to be more enlightened about this.

REFLECTIONS

1.   The story of multi-general addiction had examples of trauma in childhood for three generations. The grandmother felt unsupported by her family, her daughter had a mother with alcoholism and a father dying from AIDS and who had multiple addictions and the grandchildren experienced their mother's abusive relationships and addiction. Adverse Childhood Events (ACES) and resiliency strategies are important to focus on for individual's health.

How can we do a better job of recognizing traumatic childhood events and most importantly teach ways to be resilient without using alcohol or drugs to cope?

2.   Families need to have resources to teach children resiliency and healthy ways of coping.

3.   Judgement and stigma of others with addiction is common probably due to not understanding addiction. Addiction goes beyond personal decisions, and it is our job as society to understand the thought process of those struggling with addiction. Having the ability to see what life is like in their shoes will help us to better prevent and treat addiction. Society should feel the need to assist those who need it, not condemn them for something we don't understand. What are ways you can support that message?

CHAPTER 2

The Crisis Within Me

Story Retold by Carla Lautenschlager and Mary Ellen Wright

A story of a mother that gave up being with her children due to her substance use, eventually seeking recovery motivated by her children and supportive relationships.

My Family

I am really close to my family. I come from a huge family of drug addicts and alcoholics. It's crazy, because my family is the kind of family that can use drugs and drink, while having jobs and homes at the same time. They are what some people call highly functional alcoholics and addicts. I grew up in an alcoholic home, which was considered okay at the time. That is just how it was.

My brother, sister and mom all started drug use gradually. For them, it was textbook. They started drinking first, then began smoking pot and finally progressed to doing pills. It was just a step process for them and they all followed this pattern at the same ages in their lives. They started drinking when they were about 16 or 17 years old and then began using pain medication when they were in their 20s.

I feel like I was on a different path then them. Yes, I drank when I was in high school. I remember thinking that I would not be like them, yet I ended up in the same rut, just in a different way. I feel like I started using because I had some sort of crisis within me.

Pregnancy, Marriage and Loss

During my college years I found out that I was pregnant. I literally had sex with the father one time. I just didn't think I would get pregnant doing it that one time. I got married to the father of the baby, because I felt like it was the right thing to do. He had a lot of money, so I didn't have to work and I dropped out of college. At this point, I had never used anything, I maybe drank a little bit but that was it. I was in college, active in sports and then pregnant. I didn't plan on having kids that early in my life. Thinking back, it was during this time that I feel I lost my identity.

Right before I had the baby, my dearest relative, who was my age, died in a car accident. We were super close growing up. I feel like I've honestly hung onto that tragedy, because I didn't really grieve that loss, since I had the baby soon after that his death. I had to make a choice to be happy about the baby or grieve over the loss of my loved one.

I had my second baby two years later. After the birth of my second baby, I felt again like I was losing my own identity. I felt trapped in this marriage, and in those previous few years I still never grieved the loss of my family member.

My Beginning Use

After my second child, I remember being out drinking at a bar with some friends. Someone had mentioned doing crystal meth and I was like "oh my God, no". I was offended that they even suggested it. I don't know what changed because that same night, maybe 3 drinks later, I tried it. I was hooked from the first time. I had never felt like that before. From that point, I used daily.

After starting to use methamphetamine there would be days on end when my husband and children didn't know my location. I wasn't myself. I wasn't that kind of person before using this drug. The drug made me out go of control. I had become an irresponsible person. It was probably 3 years after I first tried meth that I got charged with distribution. I went to prison for a year and seven months. The kids were with their Dad and I didn't see them for a solid year. I talked to them over the phone, but I didn't see them because my husband didn't want to bring them around the jail.

When I got out of jail, I thought I was done. Drugs wouldn't be a problem anymore, because I never thought I would be an addict. I went to a 6-month treatment program after being released from jail.

Reconciling

After my treatment, my husband and I decided that we were going to get back together. I came home and everything was good. I had my children. I got a really good job, even though I had a felony charge on my record. I just really started feeling independent.

After about one year, I began to feel that I was making my husband miserable because of my past. He never used drugs and knew that he could raise our kids by himself. He's a good person and he makes our kids happy. We both sat down one day and decided before we end up hating each other maybe we should separate while we were still friends. We just couldn't get past the events of my drug use. He didn't trust me. He had good reason not from all I did in the past. We separated and divorced the next year.

I stayed clean for four years after I got out of prison. Eventually, I started drinking, but I was really determined not to use drugs again.

I started hanging out at the bars again with people who were drinking. The drinking was a gateway to lowering my standards as to what was okay and not okay. For one year, I drank heavily every day. After one year of heavy drinking, I started using again because I was surrounded by people who were using.

Giving Up My Children Again

My kids were with me up until I started using again and on a regular basis. I went to my former husband and told him I was using again. I just wanted the kids to be in the safest place. For that reason, I didn't feel like they should be at my house. He was the best thing for them and I was grateful that I had that option. I had to uproot them again, but it was good to know that the children would be taken care of and loved by someone I could trust. After all the horrible things I did, this man never said one bad thing about me to my kids. If he weren't such a good person that could have been totally different. He never kept me away from them unless I was using and that would not have been good for them to see.

Once the kids were living with their dad, I felt so guilty. I started using even more. I didn't want to feel my lack of responsibility for just taking my kids and dropping them off, even though it was with their dad. My kids had seen me get better and now right back to this place. Within 6 months I lost my job and car.

I began selling drugs and was about to go back to jail. Selling drugs was a big part of my story because that was how I supported myself when I was using. I was good with money and would sell drugs in large quantities. Of course, this put me at risk to go back to jail. For the next four years the pattern became that I would stay clean for 30 to 60 days, then use for a couple months, and then go back to jail.

A New Partner

Years went by and I started a new relationship with a man who also used. I became pregnant with this man's baby. I wasn't in a position to have another child, but I also was not going to have an abortion. I was arrested and sentenced for 90 days when I was 4 weeks pregnant. I remembered how I became clean in jail in the past. Thank God, I only used the first 3 to 4 weeks during this pregnancy, when I didn't know I was pregnant. I did not use in jail.

When I got out, I remained clean for the rest of the pregnancy. My son was born and I continued to stay clean. I was mending my relationship with my other children who were much older by now. I felt good about where I was at this time. I became desperate to change my new baby boy's father. I wanted to get him clean, so we could make our lives better. We had never been together clean, but I don't think the baby's father wanted to be clean. He just really wanted to find a way to use without suffering any of the consequences. He was in jail when I delivered our child, and I got him out of jail a couple weeks later.

He started using again right out of jail. We had a huge argument when I asked him to leave the house, because I didn't want him around the baby while he was using. He was determined to get me on the same level as him. He didn't care about me and just kept trying to get me to use a needle. He was using heroin bad. I kept trying to get him to stop. I never wanted to use heroin because I thought using a needle would take my addiction to a whole new level.

12

I eventually succumbed and started injecting heroin for three months. Using once led to using hardcore. It took me down fast. To support the habit, we were selling it too. I lost my job, my car and my house. I got another drug sell charge. I got caught with a lot of heroin, even though I never thought I would ever sell it. When you are heavily using heroin, you just can't make clear headed decisions. I wasn't sure why I couldn't stop. I was so tired of the consequences and now I had this little baby that could be taken from me for using. I decided then I need to get help. I had to do something, so I put myself in rehab.

The family of my baby's father were very supportive. They offered to pay to put their son in rehab also. I also tried to talk him into going for rehab. He had been at his Dad's house for 10 days and said he hadn't been using. He called me to pick him up, so I did but told him I didn't want needles in the car or taking any more changes of us losing this child. He had put my sobriety at risk before and I wasn't going to let him do that again. He was angry about it. He told me as soon as he could he was going to get dope. I ended up dropping him off and that was the last time I saw him. He died the next morning from an overdose.

Starting Over

I faced a big decision after his death. I could use his death as an excuse to keep using or I could get better for my child because I was now their only parent. In this case, I didn't have my ex-husband to cushion it for me like he did with my first children. I didn't have the father of this baby, and I'm glad that I made the decision to go straight into rehabilitation. A bed became open and I went right in to the rehabilitation center.

I feel like I have done so much in the past 10 months. I have gotten myself in a good place. I am sorry it took my child's father dying to bring me to this point, but I feel like I wouldn't be here if that hadn't happened. I feel better than I did before I had my kids. I've listened to every single suggestion that has been made for me, and I have taken advantage of every opportunity that I could since I have been at this recovery center. My life has dramatically improved: I have restored my relationship with my other children, I have my youngest child. All my children have such a wonderful relationship with each other. My older children's Dad is still my best friend. He and his wife, who also have become a supportive friends, and are co-parents. They even keep my youngest child sometimes when I need them to while I go to work or recovery. The wife of my former husband calls me and says such supportive things like "we are really proud of you and you have come so far this year". It is crazy how I can have this wonderful relationship with this man that I felt trapped with when we were married. I know so many women who lose their kids into foster care because they don't have someone that can care for the children while they recover. I am so grateful that I don't have to worry about my kid's custody because of this man and his wife.

I also have the family of my youngest child's father. Their son who died was the only addict in their family and they are really embarrassed about his overdosing. They try to spend time with my youngest child, who is their grandchild. I was concerned how they were going to handle the relationship with the baby, but they have developed a wonderful relationship with him.

At this point, I don't want to do anything to interrupt the relationships I have now. I don't want to do anything to put the custody of my youngest son in jeopardy. I just could not lose him.

I felt like before to get clean, you had to separate from your kids. I hated that I was forced to leave my children in order to go into recovery. The guilt of leaving them made me relapse into drugs. This time the recovery was a place I could bring my baby and that is why I think it works for me. I couldn't bear before to separate from my kids to get sober.

Mothers, Children and Treatment: We Need More

I feel so many mothers go through the same challenge of leaving their children, which drives them to use more because of the guilt. You want to get help, but to get help you must separate from your children because so many places don't have programs that let you stay with your children. In the current system you must give up your children when you're trying to get real help or long-term treatment. I know there are 7 places that accept women with children in my state, but it's very difficult to get into those facilities because they stay so full all the time. I would really like to see more places that accept the kids with the mother. Being with my baby was a motivator to stay clean.

I've been to college three separate times for three different things. I feel now the only way I can honor the life of my child's father is by trying to help people who suffer with opiate addiction. I'm going through a peer support training right now. It is a substance abuse certificate program that focuses on crisis intervention. I feel like that's what I want to do in my life. That's my plan right now, to be a mother and help others with addiction. I have hope.

REFLECTIONS

1.   The mother in this story told of the struggle of relapse with addiction. Her final reflection was on the separation from her children when trying to get sober and in recovery. She described that as an additional factor in her use and relapse. How can programs be developed and supported that keep mothers connected to their children in recovery?

2.   The mother in this story also described her relationship with the father of her first two children and the relationship with the father of her youngest child. One relationship gave her positive support for her and her sons. The other was a negative influence on her addiction and in which she was trying to rescue the father of her baby from addiction. How are we supportive for mothers battling addiction? What is the correct amount of support we should offer to help them in their recovery? Are we part of the problem or part of the recovery?

3.   Throughout this mother's story she was motivated by her children. Her next goal is to help others with addiction on behalf of the father of her child that died with a drug overdose. Can you see where she has struggled between her addiction and protecting her children throughout her story?

CHAPTER 3

We are Mothers First

Story retold by Lauren Drum, Haley McKee, and
Mary Ellen Wright

A mother's story of addiction and recovery,
the people who influenced her, and her
found identity in motherhood.

Childhood Origins of Self Image

I am a middle child of three girls. Growing up, I was the peacekeeper of the family who wanted to take care of everybody. I made sure that we stayed out of Mom and Dad's way. My father was an alcoholic, and my mother abused pills throughout my childhood. I also have a perfectionist older sister and successful younger sister. People used to talk about how beautiful my sisters were, but never me. I was bullied by my peers at school, and even my own sisters would say I was ugly.

Ever since I was little I have been extremely empathetic, but my empathy came at a price. It made me vulnerable, insecure and sensitive. The comments from my sisters and my classmates really affected me. I grew up with low self-esteem and was very self-critical. Now that I am older, I'm a different person. I have a lot more self-confidence, but I still remember how I struggled during my childhood.

My mother has always had problems. Members of my family and I actually think she has a little bit of undiagnosed Munchausen by proxy, which is a condition that causes parents to make their children sick to gain attention. My mother didn't make me and my sisters sick, but when we were sick, she gave us attention in unhealthy ways. She would take us shopping or give us gifts if we were ill. She made being sick a positive thing and took us to the doctor all the time. Thanks to Mom, my sisters and I always believed we were sick growing up.

A First Exposure

I was a teenager when I started getting migraines. I still remember the first time my mother took me to the emergency room for a migraine, which was the first of many times. They gave me a Demerol drip. I vividly remember loving how it felt. I experienced that same blissful feeling a few years later when I took pain medication for sinus surgery.

I always thought I would experiment with substances one day– I don't know how to explain it. I always thought I was different, and I felt that my brain was wired just a little bit differently. In the back of my head, I guess, it was somewhere in my unconscious or intuition. I just knew. The rational part of me thought there's no way I would ever abuse substances because I'm not what I thought of as the typical drug user. I grew up in an upper middle class family. I got straight A's. I was on the soccer team. I felt like I had good relationships with family and friends. Then one day I was prescribed Ambien for insomnia, which opened the door to my first time abusing a substance.

College

When I finally went to college, I had the time of my life. I was finally away from my mother and free to live independently. I started smoking pot, but I never really drank too much alcohol. Drinking alcohol always made me feel sick. My friends even joked that I was the permanent designated driver of the friend group. Besides sometimes misusing Ambien, I would also abuse an anti-seizure medication to make myself really skinny. I wasn't always trying to get high when I abused substances– I had other reasons like weight loss.

By the time I graduated from school, I weighed 95 pounds. I was moody and mean because of all the medications I took during college. I was taking the anti-seizure medication for my migraines, in addition to Adderall for Attention Deficit Disorder (ADD). Because of the Adderall I couldn't sleep, so doctors prescribed Ambien for me once again for my insomnia.

After college, I had a serious boyfriend and I moved to another state with him. I stopped taking everything, even birth control. It was amazing; I felt like I was 13 again. Every morning I woke up with so much energy. I wasn't tired. I didn't have headaches. For the first time in years, I was truly happy.

Getting Married

The reality of my developing addiction came when my boyfriend, who was now my fiancé, and I moved again for his job. I was able to avoid it for a while, but not forever. Slowly but surely, I started taking medications again. I really liked my new job, but I was at a computer all day. It was so hard focusing. My wedding was also coming up, and I wanted to lose weight for the big day. I couldn't find time to exercise with my new job, so I rationalized taking Adderall again. Plus, I figured I would be able to focus better, and I would not need to eat as much. Abusing Adderall spiraled into taking other pills too, but even though I was aware I was taking more medicines than I needed, I still thought that I was pretty stable.

A New Challenge

The wedding came and went. My new husband and I enjoyed married life. He had joined a band and they were touring everywhere. I went to different concerts and festivals that he played. I was high on life, but everything about my life changed in the blink of an eye. At one music festival, I woke up and found a tick on me. I thought it was no big deal. I removed the tick myself. I thought everything was fine, but the next morning I woke up and couldn't move my arm. For some reason, I avoided going right to the doctor. I think the reason I didn't go was because of my childhood memories of my mother telling me I needed to go to the doctor and take medication for every little thing. By the fifth day, I couldn't even lift my head off the pillow in my bed. My husband had to bathe me because I was so weak. He finally convinced me to go see someone. I found out that the tick most likely caused an autoimmune disease to develop in my body. The clinicians I saw never really gave me an exact answer as to what was the cause of all of my ailments.

For three years, I jumped from doctor to doctor to try to find an answer as to why I felt this intense and constant pain. No one could figure it out.

Eventually the pain became unbearable and I snapped. I was determined to find a doctor who would give me pain medications. None of the doctors would give me any narcotics because they knew that I was going to be in pain for the rest of my life. They knew that if they gave those pills to me, I was going to become an addict. They tried to warn me about the risk of addiction repeatedly. I would continuously tell myself the lies of, "No, you won't get addicted," and "No, you'll be fine."

After seeing countless doctors, I finally found one that prescribed Percocet to me. I also had a neurologist and a psychiatrist that I convinced to prescribe me various pills. With the multiple doctors I had prescriptions for more Percocet, Adderall, and Valium. I felt so much better because my pain was being controlled. It worked for a while, but soon, a new phase of my addiction began. Every time I went in the doctor's office to get more Percocet. I would test positive for strep. Somehow, I was able to convince them I had this cough, even though strep throat doesn't give you a cough. The first time they prescribed me cough syrup with a narcotic, it was for a severe cough. After that, when I would run out of Percocet. I would ask for another prescription of cough medicine that contained a narcotic ingredient.

It's honestly so hard to be this open about my drug use. I think the reason it's so hard for people to tell their story is because we do terrible things to meet the needs of our addiction. I'm a good person, but it's so embarrassing and shameful. It affects everything and every relationship in my life.

Husband's Support

My husband has always been a non-confrontational person. I think deep down he knew I had an addiction problem, but I never told him, and he never asked. He worked in the mental health field and would tell me stories of people who were addicted to painkillers. I wanted to be healthy for myself and for my husband. I really was trying to stop abusing the drugs at this point. Without fail, every morning I would wake up and say, "I'm not going to take it" or "I'll wait until noon." I would wake up and have good intentions, but I would get sick because my body did not know how to operate without having drugs in my system. I was withdrawing. I would go to work, and I would be sweating, vomiting, and having diarrhea. After a few minutes, I wouldn't be able to handle it anymore. I'd take a pill and it would go away. I'd lie to myself and try to convince myself that the symptoms were just a side effect of the pill and not withdrawal, but I knew deep down that I was addicted, and this was withdrawal.

One day, I decided something needed to change. "What am I doing?" I suddenly thought. I realized I was about to ruin my life and my husband's life. I finally told my husband that I was not okay and admitted to my husband that I had been on Percocet for two years. I told him that whenever I tried to stop taking the drugs, I would get sick. To my surprise, he hugged me. I think he thought, "Oh thank God, now we can get somewhere." He now had hope because I finally wanted help and knew that now we could move forward. I thought he would storm out of the room or yell, but he was so happy and relieved that I finally told him the truth.

Almost right away, we found an intensive outpatient facility for me. I started getting the help I so desperately needed. Although I knew I was addicted to these drugs, I still didn't think of myself as a true addict, and I needed to come to terms with my illness. Addicts are some of the smartest people in the world because we come up with creative ways to cover our tracks and deceive ourselves and our families and friends. I was in denial because I didn't want to believe that I was an addict. Someone in my therapy group even opened a bar to cover up his alcoholism– we do whatever it takes. My therapist knew I needed help, and he was straight with me. He told me that I had a very severe problem. It took a long time for me to accept that, and even now, it's still hard to say that I am an addict.

A New Temptation

While I was in the outpatient recovery program, I faithfully went to individual and group therapy. Recovery is such a difficult process, and I relied on the people I met in the sessions I attended. It helps to have someone who understands how difficult addiction is to overcome. I became good friends with a girl at Narcotics Anonymous (NA) meetings who had just gotten out of rehab.

I started driving her to the meetings and we became close. Both of us didn't really have a ton of close friends, so we started hanging out a bit outside of NA. One night, I invited her over to my house. To my surprise, she brought heroin with her. When she asked if she could shoot it up, I told her she wasn't allowed to shoot heroin up in my house. Then she asked if she could shoot up cocaine. For some reason, I was fine with her using cocaine but not fine with her using heroin.

The only injection I've ever given myself is for my autoimmune condition. I've never been an intravenous drug user, and I didn't even watch her do it. I wasn't afraid of needles, but I didn't watch. Even more than the needles, I was scared of myself. I didn't want to know how to do it and tempt myself with that knowledge. I was afraid I would abuse substances by injecting.

Right after my friend shot up the cocaine, she convinced me to drive her to a bad part of town to buy more drugs. It took her probably more than two hours to convince me. Once she told me she could get me some Xanax, I agreed to take her to the bad part of town to buy drugs. The entire time I was driving there, I was freaking out inside. I used to volunteer helping underprivileged children in that part of town. I've seen lots of guns and other things in the neighborhood where we were getting drugs. Since my husband was gone that weekend, I didn't want to end up in a bad situation all by myself.

When we got back to my house, I smoked some heroin and took some Xanax with my friend. After that, I have no memory of that entire weekend. Apparently, I drove two states away and went to a country music concert for a different friend's birthday. I also went on a shopping spree and spent thousands of dollars. Thankfully it was only a couple thousand dollars, but my husband and I are still paying that off. That was such a low point in my addiction. I still can't believe I drove so far away and back with no memory of it. I couldn't believe that I had done those things and let someone bring hard drugs into my house. That weekend, I went to dark places I never thought I would find myself.

Starting Over in Recovery

Telling my husband and my therapist about what happened that weekend was one of the hardest things I've ever done. Using heroin meant that outpatient therapy wouldn't be enough for me anymore– I would have to detox and do inpatient therapy to truly get better. Detoxing off the medications and drugs was such a horrible experience. Besides the symptoms of a typical drug addict withdrawing, I swelled up like a balloon and gained over

20 pounds in water weight.

When my husband took me from the detox center to the inpatient recovery center, he took one look at me and said, "you're back." He didn't mean it like I was back home from detoxing. He went on to say that my spirit was back in my body and the sparkle was back in my eyes. He started crying, and I started crying. I knew the next month and a half of rehab was going to be so difficult. Seeing how much my husband loved me made every second of the pain and hardship completely worth it.

For those 45 days, I technically wasn't supposed to see anyone, even my husband. But once each week I left the recovery center to see a doctor about my pain medications.

My husband was allowed to drive me to the doctor. Those few hours of time I had with him was the light of my week. It gave me the motivation and energy to keep going. It let me remember my goal of living a happy life with him.

For my recovery, my doctors determined that it was best to put me on long-term pain medications because the reason I had been abusing medications and drugs was to help with the pain associated with my autoimmune condition. We all determined that putting me on the pain medication was the best thing for my recovery and the best thing to prevent me relapsing. Due to my autoimmune condition, the pain would probably never go away, and I needed to have a way to be able to function on a daily basis.

Although my husband and most of my close friends were very supportive of me doing whatever I needed to do to get clean and healthy again, my sister was not. She told me if I chose to take the prescribed pain medication, I would never be allowed to drive her children. For the sake of maintaining any relationship with my sister, I lied to her about the fact that I decided to take the pain medication. That was so hard for me. I've never been a good secret keeper, and I've always been the type of person that wants to get along with everyone.

When I told people in my support group about the decision to go on long term pain meds for my health, I was nervous about how they would react. Although some people understood and supported my decision, others in the group disagreed. Since I was still taking a form of medication, even though it was prescribed, they did not feel that I was truly trying to detox and get clean. They did not understand the chronic pain that I battled. I realized that despite the stigma, this is what I needed to do and what would be best for me. If other people couldn't understand that, then I didn't need them.

Pain Versus Recovery

One problem was that many outpatient recovery centers don't allow participants to take pain medications, even if they are prescribed for conditions like chronic pain associated with an autoimmune illness. It was hard for me, because I wanted the professional support of a program and knew I needed help to get better, but I also knew that I needed my prescription medicine in order to stay healthy. Finally, I found a recovery center that did allow pain medication, and most everyone was very supportive of me still being on the medications. This outpatient program was so much more intense than others, but I knew I needed to do this for myself.

Once I was doing the intensive outpatient, I was able to get a job as a nanny. I am in recovery now, but I was using when I was watching kids as a nanny once. I never was high while I was watching their kids, but I was on pain medications. I don't feel like I could ever tell my client families that I have an addiction problem. No parent wants to know that the person watching their children is on pain medications, even if they are necessary.

One time in small group therapy, we had to go around and say who was hurt most by our addiction. I feel like I should have said my husband, but honestly, it was the kids that I take care of as a nanny. It's because they don't know any better, and I would manipulate them. If I was watching children at my house, I would turn on a TV show so I could go outside of the house and smoke weed or take a pill. It just wasn't fair to them, and that was a really hard fact that I had to face and forgive myself for. Truthfully, I'm still not over it. Whenever I feel I'm in a place where relapse is on my mind, I try to remember that feeling, and I try to use that to encourage my recovery and learn from it, rather than beating myself up forever.

For the first year of recovery I was so ashamed. I couldn't even talk to friends and family about what I did while watching other people's children. Once I got past that, I focused on being healthy and forgiving myself.

24

I tried to use those bad feelings and memories as fuel to keep going in the right direction.

When I finished the intensive outpatient treatment, I decided to stop nannying and look for a job with healthcare with regular hours. I needed healthcare badly and just wanted to start moving toward a more-established, consistent career. I was able to find a job as an administrative assistant.

Becoming a Mother

The motivating factor for me to get clean was my desire to have a baby. I probably would have let my addiction continue if I hadn't wanted to become a mother so badly. The drugs were helping my pain, but I needed to get well because I wanted a child more than anything in life. I wanted to be a good mother. I wanted to raise my child better than my own mother raised me.

My husband and I were planning to wait to have a baby to allow us to save money. We wanted to establish financial security so that we could afford all of the things a baby would need. We also decided to delay having children because I wanted to be further along in my sobriety by the time I became a mother, and my husband and I needed time to strengthen our relationship. During the beginning of our marriage, as I struggled with my sobriety and addiction, my husband didn't have room to feel things. He bottled everything up and tried to be strong for me, but it took a toll on him and on our partnership. When I was stable in my recovery, he finally had room to express his emotions and became really depressed. It had been a rocky time for us, and my husband almost left our marriage. However, I found out I was pregnant a little while after starting my new job as an administrative assistant, and by that time, our marriage was doing better, and I finally felt like we could provide the stability that a baby would need.

Honestly, I didn't even think I'd be able to get pregnant. I thought that my autoimmune condition combined with the medications I took would leave me infertile, or at the very least needing medical interventions to get pregnant. Obviously, I was very wrong. I was thrilled to find out I would be a mother.

Staying sober in pregnancy was such a huge challenge because of the physical challenges. My chronic pain associated with my autoimmune disease did not stop, and on top of the pain that I normally fought daily, I also battled horrible morning sickness the whole time. I would vomit over fifteen times each day. The combination of pain and nausea was debilitating. I wanted to do the best thing for my baby, but I also knew that I needed some sort of medication to help me deal with the daily pain that always made it so hard for me to get out of bed in the morning. My doctor and I decided that I should continue taking my long-term pain medication through my pregnancy even though my baby could possibly be born withdrawing. We knew that if I did not have some sort of medication to help me physically manage my symptoms, I would take matters into my own hands and begin abusing drugs that I was not prescribed as a way to self-medicate. I decided I was going to try not to take the medication if I could help it because I wanted to keep my baby as healthy as possible, but I knew that pregnancy would be a challenging time.

Before my pregnancy, drugs had always helped me cope with physical and emotional pain and discomfort. During the stressful time of pregnancy, all my body wanted was relief. Other than the physical pain from my autoimmune condition, my reason for using the pain medications during pregnancy was also quite simple: I am an addict. The internal dialogue within myself was absolutely exhausting, if not torturous. I would struggle between my pain, the need to satisfy my addiction and the desire to do the right thing for my baby. The struggle was intensified with pregnancy, probably because my hormones were going crazy. That's why a lot of times I would end up taking the pill. When the voices inside my head kept yelling at me to just take the medication, eventually I would. Taking a pill would get my addiction to shut up, at least for a few hours.

I don't view recovery in the black and white way that many people think of addiction. For me, marijuana has never been a substance that I've been dependent on and it's never been a problem for me the way other substances have been. I don't use it for fun. To treat my severe nausea and vomiting, I used marijuana to manage my symptoms in the same way that I used Subutex and Suboxone to manage pain. I told my doctors that I was using marijuana to help my nausea and vomiting throughout my pregnancy, and they knew what I was doing the whole time. I wanted to make sure they could keep me and my baby as healthy as possible.

Later in my pregnancy, I developed preeclampsia. All of a sudden, I started getting so swollen. I called my doctor and he told me to go to the emergency room. When I arrived at the emergency room, they told me I had gestational hypertension and they recommended I get induced immediately. However, I had my baby shower scheduled for the next day, and I decided to wait. My baby did not seem to be in distress during the hospital visit, but by the next morning, she was not doing well, and I hadn't felt her move in quite a while. I rushed to the hospital to get induced, and we found out my kidneys were failing, and I was in full-blown preeclampsia. After pushing for five hours, my daughter was born.

Baby's Health

My daughter did great in the beginning. The Neonatal Intensive Care Unit (NICU) respiratory team was in the room for the birth, and everything checked out great. Our friends who were there for the birth went home to rest for a bit, and my husband and I were enjoying getting to know our new daughter. I was holding her, and all was right in the world. They screened my urine for drugs, which turned out to be negative, and told me I would be allowed to breastfeed my baby. I was so excited.

But suddenly, something changed in her. I didn't hear it, I just felt it. I leaned over to my husband and asked him to listen to her breathing. I thought it sounded funny. Since I tend to be a very anxious person that frequently over-worries, I like to run things by my husband. My husband thought her breathing sounded normal and pointed out that they literally just had checked her a few minutes ago. I agreed that I must have been overreacting. I let some time go by, but I was still so nervous. Something just felt wrong. My husband eventually just told me I should call the nurse if I was worried, so I hit the call light.

When the nurse came in and listened to my daughter, I immediately knew something was wrong by the way the nurse looked at her. She called the NICU team down in less than a minute, and they whisked my daughter away. I asked if she would be back soon after they observe her. The nurse explained that she was being admitted to the NICU.

We quickly found out that my daughter had a heart deformity that affected her ability to breathe. Over the next few days, she began losing weight rapidly, and they wouldn't let me go to see her because I still needed magnesium to treat my preeclampsia. When I was finally allowed to go see her, I tried to nurse her, but they made me stop because she was too tired to eat. My milk never came in all the way. I hated not being able to breastfeed her. She was yellow with jaundice and she was in a bilirubin-blanket for a while. They had a tube in her nose for oxygen and lots of tubes and IV's coming out of her little body. It was so scary.

Finally, she started to do a little better. They took her oxygen tubing out of her nose and moved her into the transition room in the NICU, and we could stay with her. Going to the transition room also meant they were watching her and hoping to send her home soon. Although she was starting to do better, I definitely was not. I had barely slept for the past two weeks, and we were only allowed to hold her for 15 or 20 minutes at a time. I started freaking out so much that my husband was begging the nurses to tranquilize me. Not holding my daughter, not being physically next to her, felt so biologically and instinctively wrong. I was also physically so uncomfortable: my legs were bleeding and chafing from the swelling. I couldn't fit any shoes on my feet, and I had to go out and buy slippers that were bigger than my normal size, just so I could wear something to walk around the hospital. I got through each difficult day with the knowledge that we were so close to the day when we could take our daughter home. However, that did not go exactly according to plan.

The night before we were supposed to bring her home, about two weeks after she was born, we were told by the NICU night nurse that my daughter was experiencing intense withdrawal. Up until that point, she had been doing wonderfully and showed no signs of withdrawal. I was so hopeful she wouldn't need methadone. After all, I was just taking the medication that was prescribed by my doctor for my chronic pain. Methadone is given to babies to help them wean off of the medications their mothers during pregnancy if they start showing signs of withdrawal. She showed almost every sign of withdrawal. I was so torn up about it because I wasn't there with her to witness it myself. It made me feel like a failure of a mother even though I had known she probably would have to go on the medication. It rocked my world. It was horrible.

New Priorities and Outside Judgement

As my pregnancy progressed, my life had become more and more about my daughter. My choices and my decisions were now all about her.

The second they had put her in my arms, my priority was her future and her wellbeing. If people knew that my daughter had to go on methadone after birth, she would be judged for the rest of her life.

My family does not know that I was taking Subutex during pregnancy and that my baby needed methadone for withdrawals because we don't want her to live with the stigma associated with methadone later on in her life. However, we had some close calls with my family finding out. Healthcare workers would leave papers lying around that said things about me smoking and taking Suboxone during pregnancy or about the baby's methadone next to her warmer in the labor and delivery room. I expressed to all the healthcare workers that I did not want my family finding out about my drug use and the baby needing methadone. I wanted to make sure that my privacy was preserved. We had to convince my parents that the hospital had extremely strict confidentiality policies and that the only people allowed in the room when the child is being discussed are the biological mother and father. Only my mother-in-law knew I was taking the Subutex during the pregnancy, and when she came to see me in the hospital, the first thing she asked me about was if the baby was sick because of the medication. I could feel her judgement so intensely.

I don't know if we'll ever tell our daughter that she was on methadone as a baby. I don't want to lie to her, but I also don't want the stigma of her history to affect her. I think we'll have to see what kind of a kid she becomes. We need to know her personality and how she takes things. We need to see how sensitive she seems. Will it make her feel like she's less than normal? She is always going to know that Mommy is an addict, and she's always going to know that addiction is in her family. She'll always know those facts and that addiction is a disease. But I don't know yet if, when, and how we'll tell her about the methadone being given to her as a baby.

During my pregnancy, the doctors had performed a standard toxicology screen on my urine. Because I was taking my prescribed, long-term pain medications, the Subutex showed up on the screen. I thought that because the medication was prescribed for my chronic pain, it wouldn't be a big deal, but I was wrong. I found out that if pain medication shows up in a urine screen, a baby's cord tissue is automatically tested for other substances after she is born. Thanks to this rule, my daughter's cord tissue was tested, and since I had been smoking marijuana up until the beginning of my third trimester for the morning sickness, that showed up in the results. I didn't realize my baby's umbilical cord would be tested for the presence of drugs, or I would have stopped smoking earlier. I didn't want the marijuana to show up in her umbilical cord tissue test because it would automatically cause a report to be opened with social services.

Making a Safety Plan

Department of Social Services (DSS) came by our house twice to follow up after my daughter's birth because her cord tissue tested positive for marijuana. I was nervous because I saw DSS as a threat to my custody of my baby, and I thought they would not understand my situation. I was scared that they would judge me and make me feel like a bad mother. Surprisingly, the DSS caseworker was very kind. I told him my whole story of my chronic disease and my history of addiction and how I had been using marijuana medicinally for my pain but how I had stopped in the third trimester. He explained to me that DSS does not want to take kids away from families, they just want to keep kids safe. They worked with me to develop a safety plan so that I can smoke and make sure my daughter is safe. I showed him where I was going to smoke outside of the home in a shed in our backyard and told him that we would always have an unimpaired caregiver around for my daughter. I obviously did not smoke pot while there was a DSS case open. Even though he said it would be acceptable, I was not about to risk anything concerning my daughter. That would have been crazy.

Occasionally, I need to smoke for my severe pain, but I try not to do it too much. I smoke just enough to get what I need to make it to my baby's bedtime. I do everything I can to be a good mom and to function all day for her. I am in so much pain all day. I get home from work around 5, and if I'm having a lot of pain, I may go out around dinner time and smoke a tiny bit so I can make it through until the end of the day. I am still trying to get my pain back under control since the pregnancy when I had to go off of all of my prescription medications.

Feeling Supported

One thing I have, that most of my other addict friends do not, is really good support. My doctors are really supportive. The DSS caseworker didn't make me feel like a terrible person because I smoked marijuana in my pregnancy. I have a support system to turn to when I do feel relapse coming on, which has been a frequent feeling, especially after having a baby. Talking to my husband about feelings of relapse help me stop the obsessive thoughts in my head. Before recovery, I had to take pills the stop those thoughts and feelings, but now, I don't lie to my husband. I know if I tell him, I won't act on my thoughts. I am so lucky that I have this support, because so many people get pregnant in active addiction, in a bad situation, and without enough support. I can totally see how, if I didn't have the support I have, I would be in a very different place right now. I am very fortunate to have an amazing husband, but it is still hard feeling like other people judge me for trying to do my best in my situation. If we can help other women and mothers who don't have that support find that support early on, I think we will see better outcomes for both mothers and their babies.

Reflections on Mothers with Addiction

One crazy thing that I think is very interesting is that very few states will send babies home with methadone treatment for the baby's withdrawal. When babies go home with methadone, they are going home with moms who are addicts. Those moms could very easily use that methadone for themselves rather than their babies. But there was never a thought in my mind of ever using my daughter's methadone for myself. Never did I have any desire to try her methadone. Not once. I was thinking, and I wondered– "How is it possible to have methadone around addict moms? How do they not take it?" I've asked my therapist about it, and he agrees that he doesn't really hear about people taking their kids' methadone. It doesn't really happen. Even though the most common time for a woman to relapse is right after having a baby, most moms don't touch that methadone because it's meant to help their baby going through withdrawal.

When we use and are in active addiction, we're not directly hurting our baby. We might be hurting them second-hand if we're being neglectful as a side effect of using, but we're not directly taking away their medicine that's helping them feel better. Additionally, a lot of mothers in active addiction believe what people tell them. They come to believe that their child is better off without them anyways. They believe they are losers and can only do drugs and feel they are doing a service for their child by letting someone else parent them.

If I had to guess why mothers won't take their baby's medication, I'd have to chalk it up to our innate instincts as mothers. Even though the addiction and disease can take over our ability to parent, in our hearts and in my heart and mind my child is first. I would die for her. We as addicts know what our babies are feeling because we've withdrawn, and we're not going to take away the thing that's helping them feel better. That would be beyond cruel. I think the mother in us overtakes the addiction at that point. Deep down, in our core, we are mothers first.

REFLECTIONS

1. This is the story of a mother who was exposed to drugs as a child, and who is seeking recovery from the consequences of her parents' decisions to inject her with addictive drugs. The mother reflects on the relationship of abuse and addiction. What preventive strategies could have ensured the safety of this mother when she was a child? Why was her risk for abuse and eventual addiction missed during her childhood?

2. Many people close to her either did not provide support or were suffering from their own addictions. Her lack of relationships with friends became a motivator for her to seek recovery. How can positive and negative relationships affect seeking recovery for addiction? What should be the messages we give to families and friends on how to be supportive and promote recovery?

3. Should social support be part of every addiction treatment plan? How can social support be created for someone that can't identify a supportive people in their lives?

4. The mother in the story initially struggled to get sober, because she could not find the help that she needed. When she found a facility that could help her overcome her addiction, she became sober for the first time in ten years. How can we make addiction treatment more readily available for those seeking recovery?

5. The mother in the story was not able to see only one of her children, yet her children became the main motivator for her recovery. How can a mother's relationship with her children be supported as she seeks recovery? What is in the best interest of both the mother and the child?

Chapter 4

I Know Myself as Mom

Story Retold by Emily Guthrie and Erin Hatcher

A story of a mother who identifies the baby's well-being
as the key motivator for battling addiction
to pursue recovery.

Child or Mother

Growing up, there was a lot of drug abuse going on around me. My mother was dependent on both alcohol and drugs and was consistently in and out of rehabilitation facilities. Since my mom was absent, I was forced to act as a mother figure to my younger brother. My brother was a wild child and he got in with the wrong crowd early in his life. He used drugs and was the person that introduced me to drugs.

The first time I tried drugs I was a married teenager with two children. I was middle school aged when I gave birth to my first child. The father of my child, who I eventually did marry, was eight years older than me. When I was young, my future husband acted as a father figure. He kept me out of situations with my mother. Now that I'm older, I realize the relationship with him was actually abuse. What early middle school aged child can give real consent to having sex? However, at the time I felt it was a consensual relationship. I wasn't using drugs at the time that I had my first two children with him. I didn't get an abortion. I raised my son. I nursed him and I took care of him. No one found out about the children or our relationship. I kept the identity of the father of my children a secret. It wasn't until after we got married that anyone knew that he was the father of my children. We kept our relationship secret for over three years, until it was legal for me to apply for a marriage license. If anyone had known about the children before we were legally married, then he would have been sent to prison. Thankfully, this did not happen. Thirty days after my birthday, we were married.

A First Try

After I was married was when I tried drugs for the first time. At first, I hated even the idea of drugs, because I watched my brother on the streets trying to chase a high. But one day I became so frustrated, that I asked him what drugs were about. That same day, when I was early high school aged, my brother gave me my first high on methamphetamines. I remember being terrified. My heart was racing. I called my mother to tell her what I had done. I knew she was very well aware of the effects of methamphetamines. I took her advice of drinking a glass of milk and laying down. My mother told me to never use again.

Deportation

I became pregnant with my third child soon after this first exposure to drugs. My husband was the father of my three children. He was from Mexico. After the birth of my third child, he was deported to Mexico, because he did not have a green card. This was the third time that he was deported. He was exhausted and couldn't take being deported again, so he wanted me and the kids to move to Mexico to be with him. He told me he could not cross the border anymore. The situation became real to me. I either could join him in Mexico or raise the children alone. I chose to raise the kids alone.

Raising Children Alone, A Loss and Sinking into Drugs

Raising all my young children alone was never easy. When my daughter got older she would tell me that I was a wonder woman, doing everything a mommy does and everything a daddy does. I was working, taking care of the house, cooking, laundry, children's school needs, everything.

I had tried methamphetamine that time with my brother and did not liked the way it made me feel. I definitely wasn't dependent on drugs, but life happens. This is kind of where my story of drug abuse begins. It was at this time that my addiction took over my life. I had just given birth to my youngest child and was now raising six kids alone.

My father got really sick. He had been shooting cocaine and it messed his heart up. It emotionally messed my heart up as well. My father was everything to me. So, when my father was given six months to live, I started using drugs to hide the pain. He died that year and instead of dealing with his death, I used more drugs. When my father passed away, I was really high on methamphetamines, and my children were with me at home.

Soccer Mom with Addiction

I hid my addiction from my children. I felt kind of like a soccer mom that was just using to cope. Just using to keep going through life.

I started selling drugs to keep having the money to use them. My drug habit got very expensive. I was always in my room weighing and packaging the drugs to sell. I didn't have it around my kids, but again I had to hide in my bedroom in order not have it around them. And so over time I was being taken away from them. They were coming home from school, and knocking on my bedroom door. I would tell them to hold on or that I was busy. They weren't use to me not being attentive to them. They were used to me playing outside with them, and just being there for them as a mother. When I realized that I was starting to neglect the things I should have been doing with my children, I decided to flee the situation. I moved to____, the state where my mother lived, for some support.

Both Ways to Start Over Again

Moving helped me stay sober, and I remained drug free for years. During that time, I was the same mother that my children remembered. I would be outside playing with them, and I was working and living a functional life.

Years later, trauma struck my life again. My mother passed away and since then I have lost everything. I relapsed and also began selling drugs. When I was sober, I was going to college to become a nurse. But after my relapse, I moved to the city and was around people doing drugs and I began to struggle more.

The Result

Eventually, my drug use and lifestyle of being around others using drugs led to where I am today. At this point, my brother has kinship custody of all of my children. Department of Social Services does not allow me to interact very much with them. I am allowed to see them as long as my brother and sister-in-law are present. However, I don't really have any way to travel to see them since my brother lives in the country and I live in the city. I don't have a car. I am actively fighting to get my kids back by following all the right steps. I am currently clean and in intensive outpatient treatment at a recovery center.

For the last couple of months, I have been sleeping outside. I don't have family here, so the only people I knew were previous drug associations. I knew I couldn't go to their houses if I was trying to do well by getting clean and attempting to get my kids back. I had to sleep outside and not go to the houses that I knew drugs were being used. I was too close in recovery to relapse. Being around those people using would make me relapse.

I would walk all night and then just settle down on a bench and end up falling asleep. Usually I would awake in the morning from a car noise or something else that terrified me. But, just a few days ago was the first night that I have slept somewhere that should be stable at least for a little while. It is an emergency shelter for women. They gave me a bed to sleep in, so now my week is going to look a little different compared to what it looked like before.

As of now, I have been Facetiming my children so that they can see their Mama and see that I am doing well. They can see that I am in recovery and at the women's emergency shelter. Sometimes they can see me with my peer sponsor.

Time to Reflect

My peer sponsor has been helping me a lot because she can see that I have the will to get better. She took me to the beach over the weekend, because I have been doing so well. I struggled with going because I felt guilty thinking about not having my children with me. The only thing that is going to make me happy is being with my children. I don't want happiness from anything else; not from drugs; not from the beach, not from anything.

It was nice to be at the beach, because I was able to walk along the shore and just reflect. I believe in God. That's my faith; that's my religion. And I just thought about how God had been telling me to trust Him with my loved ones because He gave them to me in the first place. He will give them back as long as I trust in Him. He told me to know that all things happen for a reason. He is making this a time for me to be alone, so that He can re-web me in a way. He can help me to rewire the things that need to be wired in the right places to make me better.

I have found that I use drugs to hide my pain from things going on outside of the home. My kids were never the reason that I used. It has always been some sort of pain that I was feeling from loss or trauma in my life. My life is my children. Being a mother is all I know. I know myself as Mom.

During the rough times, it just seemed like it was easy to use drugs in order to hide from all the world, including all my responsibilities. The pain and struggles would overwhelm me. Using drugs seemed to take everything away. The drugs made me numb. I have realized now that when things get rough, I cannot turn to drugs. My children are looking at me and depending on me as their mother to do the next right thing. And I know if I do that, then everything will fall into place.

REFLECTIONS

1.   "It was easy to use drugs in order to hide from all the world"
For this mother drug use her way of handling stress.
How do we in society turn to drugs or alcohol to handle stress?
There is a long history of using drugs or alcohol to numb ourselves.
How can we teach children and adults other ways to handle stress?

2.   "she can see that I have the will to get better"
The peer counselor in this story was the support for the mother to feel someone believed in her. What supports are available for people with addiction to make them feel someone believes they can recover? Family members? Church? Co-workers? You or Me? Formal recovery programs?

3.   "I know myself as Mom"
The Mom in this story clearly stated that the children were not the reason for her drug use, but they are the motivation for her recovery.
Can we see the women telling the story as a mother or just an addict?
Or both?

Chapter 5

Not Wanted

Story Retold by Kelly Edwards, Molly Yost and Mary Ellen Wright

A story of a mother in abusive relationships and her journey through addiction and recovery.

Not My Friends' Childhood

As a child, I was very abused. It was not that my parents hit me or physically hurt me. My parents emotionally abused me through their words and actions. I thought that was how life as a child was supposed to be lived. Being treated meanly was all I knew. Then I discovered when I went to my friends' houses, their parents were not abusive to them. Their parents treated them kindly and spoke nicely to them. I realized what was going on in my home wasn't right, but I did not know how to fix it. My mom and dad didn't show the same love to me that my friends got from their parents. My parents didn't act like my friends' parents.

Parents with Addiction

My parents were addicted to methamphetamine. My mom and dad were struggling with their addictions. While I was growing up, my mother went to prison five or six times for methamphetamine related charges.

The First Traumatic Exposure

When I was twelve, my mom injected me with methamphetamine. I had no idea what the stuff was or why she did it, but it really messed me up. All I had really known until that point was injecting drugs was what my parents did daily. I thought that I was supposed to do drugs too. I believed that my mother injecting me with drugs was normal. I didn't know any better. Before long, I started to inject the drugs on my own. Then drugs and addiction became part of my life in the same way they were part of my parents' lives.

Too Soon

At seventeen, I became pregnant with my first child. I was not prepared for pregnancy, and I was not prepared to raise a child. With the environment I was living in, how could I have been prepared for that? I was only seventeen. I was still in high school. I did not have much support from my parents either, since their addiction was their focus. I had to grow up too soon and too quickly. Other kids my age hadn't even begun to think about having babies. I felt isolated and the whole situation put me in a dark place.

Lost Hope

A year later, my dad overdosed on methamphetamine. The overdose killed him. From that point, I just thought that was how life was going to be for me. I lost hope. I went really far off on the deep end and did not care about anything. I went crazy. It was awful. I thought that life couldn't get much worse. I saw what addiction did to my dad. Addiction changes the way you view things. Addiction changes the way you value your relationships with people. It changes your focus.

After the death of my dad, I was really stuck in my addiction to meth. Shortly after my dad died, I ended up beating a detention officer into a coma. I had to go to prison for two-and-a-half years for that offense. While I was in prison, I lost everyone and everything around me. I felt more isolated than I did when I got pregnant.

Once I got out of prison, I really wanted to get sober. I tried to reach out. I struggled to get the help I needed because there wasn't any guidance. I had already lost a lot of friends because of my addiction. I did not realize it was the drugs that were the problem. Before I thought drugs bring people together, not drive them away. It hadn't clicked that my using drugs, as a harmful way of coping, was hurting the people around me. When I used drugs people avoided me and the loneliness of that time became a motivator for me to get help.

I kept reaching out for help. I knew that was all I could do. I was stuck living the same day over and over, relying on the drugs to carry me through. I wanted to get help and I wanted desperately to get the time back that I had already lost to drugs.

A Struggling Marriage

I had gotten married while I was addicted. He was addicted to drugs too. Our marriage was unhealthy and abusive. He helped me get the drugs, when I really should not have been doing them. He encouraged and enabled my addiction. But now, we are both sober. We are both better off for it.

Not with My Children

For the past ten years, I have struggled with drug addiction, ranging from heroin to Xanax to methamphetamine. In those same ten years, I have had four children. Unfortunately, because of my addiction, I have lost them all to DSS (Department of Social Services). So, none of my children live together. My oldest stays with her father's mother. My second child stays with his father. My third child stays with her grandmother. My youngest child stays with my younger sister, who has never been in any kind of trouble. I don't have a vehicle currently, because I had lost my license, when I was doing drugs. It makes getting around difficult. I only get to see my youngest child, and it is only for one hour a week. I get my license back in August. Once I get it back, I'll be able to see her for longer than just one hour a week.

Finding Normal

As of now, I am twenty-seven weeks pregnant with my little boy. I reached out to an addiction recovery center for women; I have been sober for seventy days. This is the first time I have ever really been sober. I take classes at the recovery center and get Medicaid transportation to take me there. So far, I have taken forty classes, and I get regular drug screenings for DSS. I am working to get back on track. I have had eighteen clean drug screens so far.

I have been doing everything that I'm supposed to do: I go to the recovery facility every week day; go to church twice a week; go to Narcotics Anonymous and Alcoholics Anonymous meetings every day; and am doing

My Typical Week in Recovery:

	Monday	Tuesday	Wednesday	Thursday	Friday	Saturday	Sunday
10:00 AM							
10:30 AM				Recovery center			
11:00 AM							Church
11:30 AM		Prenatal care					
12:00 PM							
12:30 PM	Recovery center				Recovery center		
1:00 PM							
1:30 PM			Recovery center	Prenatal care			
2:00 PM						Visitation with youngest daughter	
2:30 PM							
3:00 PM		Recovery center					
3:30 PM							
4:00 PM							
4:30 PM			Church				
5:00 PM							
–	NA, AA	NA, AA	NA, AA, Church	NA, AA	NA, AA	NA, AA	NA, AA

the proper prenatal care for my baby boy.

My week is filled with appointments which take a long time to get from one to the other because I don't have a car. I save any money I have for buses and can take Medicaid transportation sometimes.

I still have more to do, but I am getting there. I don't have a job right now, but I have applied for some part time positions, one at Goodwill and one at a pet supply store. I am waiting to hear back from them. I am hopeful for the future and ready to find my own healthy normal. Doing everything that I can to recover. Doing all I can to prove I can keep my baby to the Department of Social Services (DSS) is really what is most important to me right now.

Every bit of me is focused on getting back on the straight path of being recovered. My kids have been a huge motivator to get better and stay sober. Things are really looking up for me. I'm getting prenatal care for my baby. I'm sober for the first time in a long time. I'll get my license back and will be able to see my youngest child more often. Everything is perfect. The recovery facility that I reached out to has helped me come so far. My teachers, my counselor and everybody there is amazing.

Addiction for me was feeling like I was not really wanted in my childhood. I've experienced abusive relationships. I turned to drugs to make me feel like I was wanted. I am in recovery and want my children to know that they are wanted.

REFLECTIONS

1.   This is the story of a mother who was exposed to drugs as a child, and who is seeking recovery from the consequences of her parents' decisions to inject her with addictive drugs. The mother reflects on the relationship of abuse and addiction. What preventive strategies could have ensured the safety of this mother when she was a child? Why was her risk for abuse and eventual addiction missed during her childhood?

2.   Many people close to her either did not provide support or were suffering from their own addictions. Her lack of relationships with friends became a motivator for her to seek recovery. How can positive and negative relationships affect seeking recovery for addiction? What should be the messages we give to families and friends on how to be supportive and promote recovery?

3.   Should social support be part of every addiction treatment plan? How can social support be created for someone that can't identify a supportive people in their lives?

4.   The mother in the story initially struggled to get sober, because she could not find the help that she needed. When she found a facility that could help her overcome her addiction, she became sober for the first time in ten years. How can we make addiction treatment more readily available for those seeking recovery?

5.   The mother in the story was able to see only one of her children, yet her children became the main motivator for her recovery. How can a mother's relationship with her children be supported as she seeks recovery? What is in the best interest of both the mother and the child?

CHAPTER 6

Trauma, Drama and Starting Over

Story retold by Mary Ellen Wright

A story of a lifetime of trauma, abusive relationships, drug use and starting over to regain motherhood.

My story is sometimes unbelievable to me, so I really don't know where to begin. I grew up in a family that was very involved in our church. As far as I knew, I didn't have family members who had an addiction problem or misused substances. I had many childhood traumas, but I still didn't think I would ever be an addict.

Traumatic Childhood

I experienced traumatic events in my childhood, so I guess that is where we can start this story. When I was little I played often with my dear cousin. He and I were inseparable. One day my family had to tell me he died due to an accident. I was crushed. I don't remember any help to deal with my grief, but I was very young at the time. However, throughout my life, I would question myself if my cousin would approve of what I was doing. My happy memory of him, became a conscious for me.

The other major trauma in my childhood had to do with my stepfather. He came into our lives when I was a toddler. I know my mother had been abused by him. Then when I was in my early teens my stepdad started to molest me. He threatened my life if I told anyone. I finally told my youth pastor at church and I was placed in foster care.

My teen years were spent acting out. I was uncontrollable in my behavior and just a few months before high school graduation, I ran away.

Pregnancies

After running away, I hooked up with a guy. The inevitable happened and I got pregnant. The first pregnancy ended as a tubal pregnancy, so I lost the pregnancy. I was given pain medication after the surgery. Those pain pills were the first drugs I had ever taken. I didn't abuse them though, but I remember the experience of being on pain medication.

Eight months later I was pregnant again, but this time with twins. I didn't know what to do and didn't feel I had anyone to turn to for help. I was totally ignorant on how to care for myself. I didn't understand the signs of having the baby, so my babies were born unexpectedly at home. I called 9-1-1 and tried to save them. Both babies died. When I was sent home from the hospital, I was given a prescription for pain pills from the doctors. The use of the pain pills to self-medicate was the beginning of my using drugs. After my prescribed pills were gone, I started buying pain pills on the street.

After that pregnancy, I was told I could get pregnant, but passing the baby through the scar tissue around the birth canal would be difficult. I would be considered high risk, if ever I became pregnant again. I then became a heavy user of drugs by self-medicating to numb all my emotions after the loss of the twins and then the news of my inability to have children without risk. I had so many losses at one time, I really didn't know how to cope without numbing myself.

The Next Guy

I met another guy. We lived together in a house that was full of people using meth. He eventually became physically abusive and would beat me every day. I remember one time hiding in the bushes to try to escape him. He found me though and I got "dog shit" beat. He always wanted me to use meth and I refused. After he beat me, he took me into a room and called two other guys to hold me down. They straddled my feet. He took off his belt and used it as a tourniquet. He pulled out a needle and injected me with Xanax. I was immediately high. I remember it was a different feeling and I was so relaxed. However, I was still crying. He then took me for a ride in a car and we got in an accident. As the emergency medical team treated my wounds they said if I hadn't been so relaxed, I would have been dead. My boyfriend got busted for having a meth lab and he was sent to prison for 7 years.

From that point I was shooting up mainly oxycodone and morphine for about 13 years. I got pregnant again and this time I was told about suboxone to treat my addiction. The suboxone saved my life. I did figure out how to shoot up the suboxone however, it was better than using all the street drugs.

There were times in this pregnancy that I was walking the streets pregnant, trying to find a job and sometimes trying to find a place to sleep. The father of the baby was so emotionally draining. Although he didn't blacken my eye, he really messed with my head.

I moved back to the town that my family lived. Unfortunately, the father of the baby followed me. By then he was on suboxone, but he sold them to others as a source of income.

The Department of Social Services (DSS) stepped in to make sure there was a safe place for the baby. That gave me the strength to wean myself from shooting up. I am glad DSS stepped in because I think it encouraged him to leave us alone. He did take money from me as he left, but I was just glad he was out of our lives. It took a lot of strength to stay away from my last boyfriend, but I feel I have learned how to cope with bad influences in my life.

Starting New

I have found a new way to live. I graduated from parenting classes. My DSS caseworker said this was one of the best turn arounds they have seen. I even quit smoking one month ago. I am still being treated with suboxone for my addiction, but my provider and I have been discussing a plan wean from the medically assisted therapy. I never would do that without the clinic guidance. I know people who have almost died trying it on their own.

I am surrounding myself with positive people who support my recovery. Before I was surrounded by people who just make me use more. I have a good job. I never thought I could have a job like the one I have now. I make a good living. I hope to get to have my child unsupervised when we go back to court. I live close to my family and they have been outstandingly supportive. I can't explain why I did what I did. No one in my family is an addict, but they have come to help and support me.

Finding a New Way

Part of my life transition has been learning how to handle cravings. It takes 7 minutes to get past a trigger that makes you want to get high. I have been taught and use all kinds of ways to get past that 7 minutes. I get coloring books and start to color. I have a squish ball in my hand. I am using one now while telling you my story. Seven minutes doesn't seem like a long time, but for an addict it is like an hour.

In the past the bad relationships I had were the triggers for me. I would get in a fight with my boyfriend and then go use to recover. Now I don't have those bad influences and so my triggers are much less.

The thought of being a mother and learning parenting is my main motivation now. I really think parenting classes are so important. I hope by telling my story that other people understand more about addiction. I hope we can stop some of the judgement that people put on addicts.

REFLECTIONS

1.   The story of this mother begins with childhood traumatic events. Children in foster care have experienced some type of trauma that resulted in their being placed with a foster family. How well do we support foster families in our country? Can we strengthen foster services to support the child's resiliency and the foster parents' skills caring for children with prior trauma?

2.   Poor relationships with abuse were a constant part of this mother's story. Do we adequately assess for abuse? What people could have further understood that she was in abusive relationships and how could those people have helped her?

3.   The mother in this story pointed out when she was in poor relationships, she was using substances more. When she had supportive relationships, she felt supported to recover both from family and Department of Social Services. What do you think of tough love versus being supportive for people with addiction? Is there a difference in the approach? How can we encourage more supportive relationships to foster recovery?

CHAPTER 7

You Are Worth It

Story Retold by Daniel Rafalski and Mary Ellen Wright

A story of the feeling of shame and eventual empowerment of a mother with addiction.

The Beginning

It all started in high-school. At first, I was just drinking alcohol at parties with friends. Eventually, that transitioned into smoking weed in my teen years.

I came from a well-off family. My dad was often working long hours, while my mother ran life at home. She was and has been always such a warm, comforting and supportive figure in my life. Whenever I think of my dad I am reminded of his cold and distant demeanor, mostly because he was always working or away on business trips. When he was home he never really engaged with my mother and me. As I remember, fighting between my parents started when I was 18 years old. I began to struggle to deal with the conflict. I would avoid coming home. I would avoid talking to them. I began to cope in ways that were not healthy.

After I finished high-school and left home for art school, I began to use opiates and experimented with other drugs like hallucinogens. Using such mind-altering substances seemed therapeutic. I was able to take a step back, reflect on myself and find a better understanding of where I stood in the world. The culture that surrounded the art world, when I was a student, seemed to accept the use of substances to stimulate the creative processes. In my mid-twenties, as stimulating as using mind altering substances seemed to be for me, I soon found myself moving away from those kinds of drugs.

As I became more mature and created a busy work life, I began to move away from hallucinogens. I became very successful in my field of work. Despite moving away from hallucinogens however, smoking marijuana and intravenous use of opiates persisted. Using made me feel like I was living in the moment.

I had only worked for two years before leaving my job to find somewhere I could give myself time to be clean. Unfortunately, when I had moved somewhere else, I found myself immersed in a like-minded drug community. Instead of escaping drugs, I had a whole new network of people who were using the same types of drugs that I was trying to avoid. I had set myself up for failure. Shortly after my immersion in this community, I found myself questioning my choices in life. Questioning my choices became a bit of a weird crisis.

Returning to My Mom

I ended up running off and went back to my mother, who at that point in time seemed like the only person I could count on for help. It turns out she needed me almost as much as I needed her. She was an introvert her whole life and I can safely say I am not an introvert. Because she was alone now, she became reliant on me to take her out and party together. As cool as it may have seemed, I needed her now. She didn't disappoint me. She behaved like the warm and supportive family figure she had been during childhood.

A New Partner

Fast forward a few years, I met my future partner. It's funny, when we had first met he had told me he was close to my age, so I didn't worry about his age. It was no big deal. We were messing around and fell in love quickly. It wasn't until we knew our love was mutual when he told me his real age, which came as a bit of a shock. He was quite a bit younger than me. Somehow our emotional maturity seemed to meet in the middle. He was very mature for his age. I was immature for my age. We had a good middle ground to work with in our relationship. I needed his maturity.

Getting into Trouble: A Chance for a New Start

Despite his maturity, we ended up getting into trouble together. One time my partner and I got into trouble to the point where I spent a few days in a real prison. Being in prison was one of the worst experiences of my life.

My partner's parents ended up sectioning him. Sectioning meant he had to spend thirty days detained in prison. I tried to use this experience as a learning opportunity. I had a chance to open my eyes to what I was doing with my life.

My partner felt the same. After he got out of prison we decided to go through sobriety together and act more like adults. We moved to a new place where my partner had friends we could talk to and help support our attempt at sobriety. Both our families were off and on about our decision to live together. They had been against us being together from the start. They especially objected due to the age difference and the messes we together had gotten into in the past. I understood why they felt that way. They didn't want to see us getting into any more trouble.

Once we moved we had stayed sober for the first two months without issue. In the third month we returned to smoking weed. We felt smoking marijuana didn't count. We eventually moved into a house full of guys who were friends from my childhood.

A Baby

Shortly after we started living with my friends, I started using again. It wasn't too long after beginning to use again that I also found out I had become pregnant. We both were shocked, but my boyfriend seemed particularly dazed. He had just grown out of his teenage years and had no thoughts about having a child. At first, we both had no intention of keeping this baby. It was such a crazy part of my life. I was not sober. I had been using pills on and off for the first two weeks of pregnancy. I continued to use afterwards, because I did not think we were keeping the baby.

I decided a few weeks after finding out I was pregnant to go home to visit my family. During the visit I had time to think. I realized that moving out and away from my childhood friends to a new location was the right choice. I wanted my partner to move with me. I also realized that I needed to keep the baby, whether my partner was going to be by my side or not. I hoped, however, that he would be there for the baby.

I really lucked out with my partner. After telling him of my new intentions of keeping the child, he supported me and welcomed the idea. Once we returned from visiting family, we had moved into a new building and found ourselves a roommate.

Following Temptation and Breaking Away from Temptation

We eventually learned our roommate would regularly take psychedelics with her boyfriend. We began finding it too easy to say, "why not use?" when we were around them. This proved to be quite challenging at times. We had continued smoking weed and I continued taking pills for a few months.

At a certain point I began to tell myself that I needed to get serious. I had a life in me that needed my care. Then and there I committed myself to be the healthiest I could be for the rest of my pregnancy. After the third month of being pregnant I lost the desire to smoke weed or cigarettes. The smell became repulsive.

I had to keep myself and my child healthy. Around the sixth or seventh month of pregnancy I began to struggle to eat. I began to have to set reminders to drink water on my phone because I would often be dehydrated. It was terrible. It was in this same month when I decided to start smoking weed again. I needed to eat something for the child and smoking weed was the only way I could work up any appetite.

As my pregnancy progressed I felt more and more connected with being pregnant. I started developing and processing the feeling that this pregnancy was going to change my life forever. The whole process of feeling fat the first few months, then feeling flutters and realizing there is a living, moving being inside me, it was surreal. I felt bad about using weed to eat, but I truly felt that the ends justified the means, I had to feed myself and my child

In the last few months of the pregnancy I began to attend pregnancy group meetings where everyone was around the same gestational age. I was so excited about these groups. Even my partner would go with me and learn things that we had never even thought about regarding having a child. It was special being in that group, especially when you can experience it with other women who are in the same mindset and all due around the same time.

For some time, it had seemed like we were going in an upward trend regarding our lives. A couple weeks before the birth of our son, my boyfriend ended up relapsing hard. He ended up getting in trouble and being put in jail. I had to bail him out.

Our upward trend dramatically changed. My boyfriend, the father of my baby, couldn't believe he was having a child so young with someone so much older. It got to him. I was very understanding by putting myself in his shoes. I wish he could have pulled himself together since we were so close to having the baby. I needed him to stay true to his commitment. In the end however, I let him know that I was ok. I told him that I still loved him, and understood his position.

Once my son was born and was about a month old, my emotions were rampant. I began to feel some regret that I had continued smoking weed while I was pregnant, especially given that I wanted to stop completely. I was frightened they would find THC, from marijuana, in my breast milk and take my son. I was so scared that I stopped smoking weed immediately after my son was born. When my son's umbilical cord tissue was tested there was nothing found, which made me happy and relieved.

After the incident of my boyfriend's extreme doubt before I gave birth, I wondered if my boyfriend would ever be involved with the baby. When the baby was three months old he began to settle down and come to terms with having a child. He was amazing. He would take care of our baby and even split nights with me, so I could sleep. He really is an amazing guy, I wouldn't have been so lenient with him if he wasn't such a big help and stayed so committed. It was a crazy couple of months.

When I continued to go to the pregnancy group I would hear and see women coming in who weren't fortunate enough to have a partner like mine. I remember thinking, "being a single mom, I couldn't do it". My boyfriend really became involved and I didn't feel like a single mom. When the baby was three months old, I had stopped using any sorts of drugs because I wanted to breastfeed. It was a great time.

Falling Back In

I soon found myself falling back into marijuana after feeling achy and cramping often. I figured it was not too big of a deal. Not too long after this, what had been going great, seemed to all fall apart again.

It started when my boyfriend had ordered benzodiazepine off the internet from a research company. The substance he ordered wasn't even FDA approved but it was supposed to be like Xanax. I had never really delved into pills like Xanax and benzodiazepine. That type of drug was never really my thing. These types of drugs were his thing.

After taking a few, he completely blacked out for seventy-two hours. In those hours we ended up having a domestic dispute incident. He became very violent. I had never been so scared. I felt lost. We were all we had, and I had no idea what to do.

Getting Help from Child Social Services

The following attempts to reach out to him after he was put in jail were chaotic to say the least. I ended up having Child Social Services (CSS) get involved, because our child was home when the incident occurred.

You never hear a good story about government people showing up to your house, but I wanted them to come. I wanted to tell them honestly about our drug use. I wanted them to know about what my boyfriend took and how he has never been a violent person prior to this incident. I wanted them to know that he is amazing and nothing besides the drugs he took that day made him act the way he did that way. When I did get a chance to talk to an investigator, she asked a lot of questions about me, especially regarding my use of drugs.

During my questioning, she reminded me about a program they offer which involves a substance treatment and recovery team. They help you and allow you to go through the program with your child and partner. The investigator also mentioned that we would be attending lectures and periodic drug screens would be done in this program. Upon hearing this, I panicked. My partner had not been sober in the past thirty days, and I had been smoking weed. I hadn't told the investigator that I had stopped breast feeding.

When these team meetings started my partner and I were separated. He was in jail at the time. The only communication I had with him was through a third party. For what felt like the longest time I had been alone at home with our child. I missed him.

When he did eventually get out of jail my partner ended up at a sober house that was more like a frat house than the purpose of being a recovery house. The person who runs it was one of my partner's friends. I should have seen that this was bad news waiting to happen, but I didn't think anything of it at the time. Little did I know that I would eventually pay heavily for not seeing what was coming down the line, but I will share that later.

I still felt quite on edge when we had our first meeting with the Children's Social Services (CSS). They provided us with a large team of people who were encouraging us and whose purpose was to keep us out of court and provide support in our trying times.

I did not want to reveal anything to them or do a urine screening to avoid the shame of drug use. However, at the same meeting I did end up revealing that I had slight amounts of THC in my system. The investigator was shocked, since I had not told her that when we first met. She told me I had been dishonest with her. I never really felt too pressured or shamed by the investigator, which was kind of her. However, I still felt a little ashamed especially given that I still had THC in my system. I was screened the following week.

After the first couple weeks of meetings I was able to take a break and went back home to our families to show them our child. Despite still having a bruised eye, I was able to get the no contact lifted, so I could talk to my partner while I was away. He was still at the sober house. It was a nice break from the chaos while it lasted, but upon my return, it began feeling like it was all falling apart.

Returning to my meetings I was very quickly accused of lying to them. I was reminded of the THC in my system and they also found Kratom* in my drug tests. I had taken Kratom when I was in pain. Kratom looked legal and not like too big of a deal at the time, but I had come to realize that at this stage of my recovery, that is still using. *Kratom – similar effects like opioids, may be addictive; illegal in some states.

Visitation for the Baby and Father: Wrong Supervisor

One of the team members had told me that my son was finally able to visit his father at the sober house. The visitation plan required an official supervisor had to be present during my son's visitation with his father. The appointed supervisor is approved to look after our child. Our investigator had been pushing for the owner of the sober house to become one of the supervisors, that way we could leave our child at the sober house if my partner and I wanted to leave together for a little while. At the time, it seemed like a great idea for not only us, but the owner of the sober house. Being an appointed supervisor would reflect well on him and his recovery house.

I was initially told by my support group members that there was no way the owner would be approved to be a supervisor. He had drug chargers two years prior and I was told that you need at least 10 years without any convictions, especially drug convictions to be an approved supervisor. This should have been a red flag from the start,

The arrangement seemed too good to be true. Believe it or not, after some time, the owner ended up getting approved to be the supervisor for visitation. The approval also allowed him to supervise our visitations and also to watch our son independently.   I was very surprised, and happy to have someone other than myself watching our child. At the same time, I was nervous leaving my son at the sober house. I did not know the owner that well or whether he was comfortable having a baby around. Having a baby possibly sleeping there too. I had really pushed aside all my natural instincts telling me that the whole situation felt wrong. I felt like I was being tested. After all the process approved him, so there must have been some good screening done. I almost feel as though I had been set up for failure in a strange way.

Honesty

Around the same time as getting the supervisor approved, the investigator contacted me saying that they know I lied to them about my use. They set up a hair follicle test for my son and me. I was totally fine and willing to do the drug testing. I told them what they would find. I was completely honest. I was through with hiding and lying. I told them they would find my prescriptions, the anxiety medications, the medications they gave me in the hospital. There was no point in lying, it would only lead to more trouble. I told them everything. When they got around to asking me what they would find in my son's hair I was straightforward and said the only thing they might find was THC because of my breast milk. I was 100% certain at the time and had no doubts regarding my son.

My hair follicle drug test came back completely negative. They asked plenty of questions regarding certain shampoos, whether I dye my hair. I answered all of them truthfully. It turns out it was totally negative due to my hair dye. I told them once again what I have in my system. I reminded them what they knew I have in my system from when they screened my urine. I reinforced that I had been honest with them since my urine test and thankfully they took my word for it this time around.

An Unexpected Result

My son's follicle test took a bit longer to come back. When I asked my peer support group about why it was longer than mine, they told me it usually takes longer when there are positive results in the test. Upon hearing this I wasn't worried. I figured it was just the THC from my breast milk, which I had already told them. If it was only the THC, we had a plan with our Child Family Team. The plan included that my partner and I could move in together with our child if we took domestic violence courses. I thought the plan was great. It was what I was expecting. I was ready to move forward.

My son's follicle test finally came back a few days later. My son's hair follicle tested positive for THC, but more importantly, it came back positive for cocaine as well. I was absolutely shocked. Cocaine is one of the drugs that I absolutely had not taken since my mid-twenties. I never was even tempted to take it since then and I know my partner had never been a big fan of it either. This is when our situation really started to deteriorate.

After getting the results of my son's follicle test I was then court ordered to go into recovery. I was made to do an outpatient program with my son. At the end of the first meeting I attended, I was approached by a couple of people who told me to report to the Child Social Service office. My partner and I were then separated for what they said were legal reasons. So, there I was sitting in a room being told things. He was in another room being told other things. Finally, the investigator asked me why the test came back positive for cocaine in my son. I was pissed, shocked, and appalled. You name it. I had no idea where the cocaine had come from. No clue as to where it could have originated or why the levels were so high. This was one of the worst experiences of my life. I was beside myself.

The Decision

Within 10 minutes since the start of that conversation, they told me I needed to "make a decision". They told me I could either go to a sober house, or I could put my son in foster care.

How my son was exposed was rattling my mind. I couldn't wrap my head around it. I wondered about how he was exposed to so much, where he was exposed, you name it. I thought there was no possible way. I know for a fact that I was there for my son and if not, the supervisor was watching him. If he didn't, there were always girls over at the house who would meet my son and play with him. He was never not in view of someone. When with me, he was always in my sight. These thoughts clouded my mind.

When I was told I had to choose foster care or this Christian sober house, I panicked. I had been doing well enough with my sobriety. I had been going through the process of recovery like I was told. Now they are telling me I needed to take a step back and get even more "help". I began having a mental breakdown thinking about being forced to do Christian based everything at the same time as trying to stay clean, and having no contact with your partner. They also take all electronics at six o'clock. You are not allowed outside for the first 90 days, with no cigarettes and no medications even if prescribed for you. I was raised with one parent being Jewish and the other Catholic, so I had a good knowledge of God and religion. I never really attended church. I think everyone has their own way of viewing God and my way doesn't involve looking at it as some religious figure. I just have an issue with it.

I felt as though my mental health would be broken if I attempted being admitted to the Christian based program. The pressure of being in that program would be a trigger for me to use again. I know I would use again. I don't want to be in that kind of a place in front of my son. My only other option is foster care. At this point there was nothing else I could think besides "you've got to be kidding me?"

You've got to remember, this was happening during the one meeting where my partner and I were placed in different rooms. The Children's Social Services investigators kept having to go back and forth to discuss the options to both of us. Finally, I concluded that, despite not being able to see my son as often as I would like, I needed to get myself right. Maybe I could take the time to do this and eventually be in a place where the government can trust me, and I could trust them.

To add insult to injury, around the same time as the meeting, we had found out that our supervisor, who watched the baby had been convicted of selling cocaine two years prior. He was still approved and appointed to be our son's supervisor. This was a horrible situation. I felt everything was getting worse and worse. So long story short, at the end of the meeting we decided our son was going into foster care. After 10 minutes the foster parents came in. They were amazing people. I couldn't have asked for a better couple. They were both artists, like I am. They both stay at home for their jobs. They don't have any other kids at home. It was a bright spot in an otherwise dreary situation. I remain very thankful for them.

At the time of giving him up to the foster parents, my son was only four months old. It was tough on me. I thought I was going to be missing all of his firsts. However, I knew it was the best for him and for me in the long run. I was busy going to substance addiction groups as well as accepted care therapy. I still go to these meetings 5 days a week to focus on my recovery while continuing my passion for art.

My partner was in treatment 3 days a week. He also voluntarily joined a domestic violence class. I am proud of the fact we both want a successful recovery. Especially the way my partner took initiative and responsibility. He wanted to make up for what he did to me and consequently our baby. He was amazing throughout the whole process. I felt, and to this day still feel, very lucky to have someone like him in my life.

61

My son is still a big part of who I am and how I got to this point. There is a happy ending to this story. Although that day I had to choose between foster care and a sober house was one of the worst days of my life, it ended up being a blessing in disguise. I think it is really important to go through that whole anger and ending up sort of surrendering to the inevitable when it comes to getting clean. I think that it was really an opening to reality. I had to face the real issues - that I need help and time for myself to understand addiction and staying clean. I have met so many incredible women. I found that I am understanding myself so much better. I have been empowered. I enjoy sobriety to the fullest.

We went through a lot of emotions with visitations at Department of Social Services (DSS) offices. The supervisor spoke of us as never missing a meeting at any time, and we went to every class.

My son has just been growing and growing and growing. His foster parents and I share a parenting journal that we have been recording after every visit. My partner and I keep in touch with the foster parents and make sure that our son sees us enough and in the right way.
Someone was telling me the other day, the shame of being a mom and having these issues and realizing, "oh my god, I am missing all these months with my son".

When I do see people in my focus group in the Department of Social Services (DSS) offices, I didn't want to let them know that DSS took my son. I have finally come to terms with that fact.

Reflecting by the Mother in Recovery

I am not ashamed at myself for something that really changed my life for the better. It is amazing how far I have come. I am proud of myself. I am proud of my partner. I am very blessed to have gone through this. Speaking about it I think is really empowering, especially going through this as a mother. I think it is really important for other mothers experiencing substance abuse to not feel ashamed of something like this, because it comes down to a matter of choices with addiction being like a disease. It is something you have. Unlike other diseases, you are the one who makes the choices to put it into remission, because you can make it better. You don't have to feel helpless. You do have the power to get over it. It really has been like a reality check for me as a person. The experience has made me and my partner members of the sober community.

I am not ashamed to speak about my addiction. I really hope my story reaches women who are struggling and helps them not feel that ashamed for having the disease of addiction. I want them to know that they can make choices to help themselves and those they care about. I want them to know that if they are working hard during their recovery and if they really want it, sobriety is achievable.

I think that all too often, women feel ashamed if they are a mom. They label themselves as just an addict mom. Yes, I am a mom. Yes, I am an addict, but I am an addict in recovery. I am not just a singular label. I think women especially put themselves in a position that I am a mom, so I have these crazy expectations of myself. You must stop trying to live up to expectations that aren't realistic. You need to try to set a goal for yourself and don't let other people get to you.

Don't give in to the shame. Let it drive you. A very good friend of mine told me, sometimes you must lower your expectations. You will enjoy people and yourself a lot more. People can suck, and if you are expecting people to always act a certain way, you are making yourself feel like crap. You are going to try to live up to these unrealistic expectations of yourself, which is only going to make you feel miserable. That's not fair to you or those closest to you.

It's a shame that people shame others for things that they go through. It's a shame that people feel embarrassed about something if they are trying to get help. It's awful that people set these expectations of themselves and what societal norms seem to dictate. Then they overwhelm themselves and it pushes them back into using.

I think that by sharing stories and knowing that people have success in sobriety helps others. It's a "you are worth it" type of thing. I always keep going back to what's best for my son and what is best for my own personal headspace. It wouldn't have worked for me the way it had if my partner was not fully all in recovery with me. I would've had to do it all on my own, which I would have done. Having a partner who was just as engaged in this effort to better his life, and consequently better mine, was important to me. The two of us are utmost providing for our son.

63

Our son has a right to have a mom and a dad and he needs a mom and dad who are sober. He needs that feeling of love. I don't want to ever be too stoned where I ignore him or am too tired or lazy to be there for my son.

Kids know. I knew when I was growing up with my father that he really wasn't there for me. I never want my son to feel that way. I hope that my son knows he is loved. I hope he never has to know he was in foster care. He is young so maybe that will be true. I want to associate and keep in touch with the foster parents, if they want to stay in touch.

It's been a surrendering of power and control which ultimately has made me a better person all around and a better mother. I'm happy to share my story and I am really glad to have an audience.

REFLECTIONS

1.   Social context played a role throughout the mother's story. She even reflected on addiction and social context. What ways could social context be addressed as a prevention for relapse? What ways could social context be addressed as a prevention for initiating substance use?

2.   Support of her partner was important to this mother. What are your reflections on the relationship?

3.   The support from Children's Services seemed pivotal to the story. What were the positive and negative parts to that support as seen by the mother?

4.   The mother in the story used Kratom for pain because she thought it was a legal substance and therefore didn't count as a substance that could be a problem. How can we let everyone know that any substance you use whether legal, illegal, herbal, natural, prescribed or not prescribed may affect you and your children?

5.   The mother and foster parents are sharing the care of the child currently. What ways could parents in recovery continue to learn parenting skills and be involved to prepare for the possible reunification with their child?

CHAPTER 8

I'd Be Dead Without My Grandson

Story Retold by Olivia Chafe, Jacob Estrada, Heide Temples, Mary Ellen Wright

A story of a family affected by addiction and tragedy told by the grandmother

Background

I was a mother of four when I was only twenty years old. When I met my husband, he had two baby girls. The mother of his baby girls was not around. So, I raised and loved them as my own. Before long, we had three daughters and one son. Life had begun for us.

The Start of my Addiction

I had issues with my knees for a while. The discomfort finally needed medical attention, so I went to the doctor. The best option for me would be to undergo surgery in hopes of a long-term solution. With operations come pain, and I was prescribed pain pills to handle the pain. As luck would have it, I got addicted. As the doctors increased my dosage, my tolerance for the pills effect continued to rise. Eventually, I was finding pills to meet my need. Looking back on it, I'm sure that it must have affected my family. I was raising our children during the time I was using pain pills. The whole time, I just didn't realize what effect it may be having on our family. I finally put the pain pills down and refused to take them anymore.

A Tragedy

My son and his friends went joy riding. It wasn't until they were riding downhill that they discovered the brakes were broken. I never expected to receive the call that my son was in a serious accident. The caller continued to report that he was taken to the emergency room and was fighting for his life. I was so scared at the hospital waiting to hear his condition. I didn't think the situation could get any harder. Then the doctors came out to the waiting room to break the news that my son was braindead. Everything went black. My baby, my dear son was braindead.

I was desperate. I felt a strong urge to save my son, but no amount of fighting was going to change his condition. He was dying. I had to give him up. The doctors let me say my goodbyes while he was still taking breathes and his heart was still beating. We made the decision, in the midst of this, to donate his organs to save other lives. So, I guess something good came of it, if that can be some sort of consolation. It was hard walking away. I hated leaving him. The doctors say I have Post Traumatic Stress Disorder (PTSD) from the experience. I replay the phone call of him being hospitalized over and over in my head. It's not that I want to, it just happens

My Oldest Daughter

My son's death hit all of us hard, but my oldest daughter was especially saddened by his death. She was very close with him. She had a baby boy of her own. He acted just like my son used to act. He had my son's eyes and everything. She can't bear to look at old pictures or reminisce with the rest of the family when we laugh about the memories. It tears her apart. She copes by drinking a lot and smoking pot to make it hurt a little less.

When she got pregnant again, she knew it was time for change. That's how it works, when babies are coming, we put their needs first. They are more important than whatever struggle is caused by our addiction.

My Youngest Daughter

Meanwhile, my youngest daughter was struggling with an addiction to pain pills. Having a hard time coping with her brother's death, she was on track to become an alcoholic. It was a hard time for all of us. To her credit, she was able to stop once she learned she was pregnant. Her baby

66

was born perfectly healthy, and she named her after her brother. I know she wishes her brother could have been there. He would have loved his new niece.

My daughter certainly loves her baby, I can hardly convince her to let me have a turn holding her. I am so proud of her. She is a good mom. But I know this is hard for her. Without her pain pills, she feels the emotions surrounding her brother's death and tries desperately to escape. She still smokes a little pot, just to help her nerves. I don't personally like to see any drugs around right now, but, to me, this is the least of all evils.

My Middle Daughter

My middle daughter had problems with substance abuse. When her son was born, he didn't show signs of withdrawal and didn't need to go to the Neonatal Intensive Care Unit (NICU). I doubt my middle daughter used pills while she was pregnant. When there are children to think about, we try to protect them the best we can. I know she did smoke a lot and drank a little while she was carrying him. Thankfully, he was still healthy when he was born.

We lost touch with my middle daughter when she began dating this new guy a few years back. She'd been running all around the country doing - well, we don't know what she is doing. That's the terrifying part. I don't remember the last time we've heard from her. I just remember having to call her to tell her how her brother had passed away. She didn't believe us for a long time. She thought it was all a hoax to get her to come home. We eventually sent her a picture of his obituary.

There was one time we thought she would finally come home. We were looking forward to welcoming her back. She called and said she was just exhausted from working on the streets to get her next fix. She was probably addicted to everything at that point. Her grandmother bought me a plane ticket to fly across the country and bring her back where she belongs. I flew out the very next morning. I excitedly sat up all night in the airport looking around for my daughter. It had been so long since I'd seen her, and I couldn't wait to hug her. I wasn't mad at her for leaving, I just wanted her back. She never showed up, and I flew back with nothing to show for it but an unused extra ticket.

My Grandson's Early Life

A knock at the door brought a whole whirlwind of change to my home. The Department of Social Services (DSS) gave me my middle daughter's son, after removing him from his father's care. The father really tried to step up and take care of him. The main problem was that he was a drug dealer. I know my grandson saw a lot that isn't appropriate for a toddler to see, even if he didn't fully know what was happening around him.

I was devastated he couldn't stay with his parents, but I knew he would be better off with me. I still never expected to be a mother again at my age.

My Addiction Resurfaces

At this time, I was addicted to meth (methamphetamine), but I couldn't see it. I just didn't want to feel the pain of losing my son anymore. I'd rather be numb. It all started again, because someone I mistook for a friend started giving me pills here and there. At first, I didn't want to take the pills, but it's hard to say "no" every time. Gradually I started saying "no" less and less. So, when she said I should try meth, I said "yes." Meth didn't make me forget my pain; it just made me pay a lot of attention to everything else.

I know some people would have been appalled I was using meth around my grandson. I truly believed that, because I was eating it, it wouldn't affect him. I made sure not to smoke around him, and I never had paraphernalia around him. I was trying to do right by him.
Now, I know that's not how meth works. It kills me to know that the entire time I was eating it, it was coming through my skin and affecting my grandbaby.

It was a rough time for us. Our son's death hit us hard, and there are no instructions on how to handle that. My husband and I were fighting. I was still using meth. He was smoking pot, while messing around with other women on the side. DSS didn't care that I was doing my best under the circumstances; they still took my grandbaby.

Jail and Getting Clean

I pitched an immortal fit when I found out they were taking my

grandbaby away from me. I don't understand how I didn't see that coming; they arrested me. For three days, I laid in that cell and detoxed. All those feelings hit me wide open, as I was coming off the drugs
.

Everything I had been trying to ignore was now front and center and begging to be acknowledged. Coming off the meth was like taking my finger off the fast-forward button and realizing how exhausting living at that pace had been. I didn't get any help the days I was in jail, as I went through withdrawal. I mostly slept through it. It wasn't until I was out of jail that I went looking for and found treatment. Reunification with my Grandson was my goal.

Where I am Now

My grandson is a young child now and, developmentally, he is doing fine except for some ADHD. He also needs counseling, because of everything he went through. I'm trying to be better for him. I haven't touched a drug since the day before he was taken from me and wouldn't dream of it. I'm doing everything in my power to get my grandson back, because I can't lose both my baby boys. I've already lost my own son, and there's nothing I can do about it; but I can do something about my grandson. I'm not going to let my pain prevent him from coming home to be with his family.

Reunification is the goal and I'm taking every step I can to make it for him. One hour, once a week, isn't nearly enough time to spend with him. I'm tested constantly to make sure I'm clean, but it's worth it. I'm renovating my whole house, tearing up the carpets and cleaning the walls and ceiling with bleach and water. Meth gets everywhere, and I never realized that. We're working to get everything ready for him to come home. After all, I owe him a lot; without him, I'm sure I'd still be hooked on drugs or maybe dead.

REFLECTIONS

1.   The mother in this story clearly loves her children, and it is obvious how much she loves her grandchildren. For most of the women in this story, pregnancy is what jump starts the process to get clean and protect their children. With that in mind, what support systems can be implemented to give them the best chance of success to stay clean and raise their own children in happy, safe environments?

2.   This story demonstrates the cyclical nature of a family's drug addiction to help cope with devastating life events. Are there other ways to cope with pain? Is counselling available so everyone can deal with grief, and if not, why? Can the cycle be broken if the family can be taught healthy ways to cope with pain? Why did one sister have more difficulty with addiction than the others? What did the oldest and youngest sisters do to come off the drugs?

3.   The mother was arrested for drug abuse and detoxed in jail. Why aren't jails prepared to provide drug abuse treatment? The prisoners are arrested for drugs and are a captive audience. Wouldn't this be a good place to break the cycle of drug abuse?

4.   This story brings up concerns for the children involved. Will their exposure to drug use contribute to using drugs in the future? Will they repeat the cycle? Is there a better way for the foster care system to handle children of drug addicts? Is reunification with the child's family always best, when there is a history of addiction?

CHAPTER 9

Unexpected Motherhood

Retold by: Mary Ellen Wright

Story of a newly married grandmother becoming a mother due to a kinship placement of her new husband's grandchild and the love that grew

New Mother

If you had told me I would have been a new mother of an infant in my sixties, I would never have believed you. My story begins with the death of my first husband making me a widow. Many years passed before I met a wonderful man, and we decided to get married. His wife was also deceased. We shared so many common interests. We shared our faith and liked getting involved in church activities.

I felt I was living in a dream. We spent our time together completing our careers and planning for retirement. We enjoyed picnics, helping at the church, going to movies, dinner with friends and sharing daydreams of our retirement travel plans.

Ours was a blended family. I had two grown children of my own. He had one child of his own. By grown, I mean our children were in their twenties and early thirties. I had a close relationship with my two children. Unfortunately, my new husband was distant from his one daughter. He didn't even know where she was living. I had never met her. All I was told was she had problems growing up and never communicated with her father. He would leave her messages on the last phone number he had for her. She never responded to his messages. I would watch his disappointed face as he repeatedly checked his phone for days after sending his message to her. We would pray for her together. I would pray for him to find peace in his heart. Until the day that we were contacted by his daughter. She was in the hospital. She just had a baby.

The Sudden Change

Many different emotions were happening at the same time. My husband was relieved to know his daughter was even alive. I was happy for him to have that small bit of peace. I was so nervous to finally meet her. Honestly, I was scared.

We were practically silent in the car going to the hospital. We only spoke to assist each other with directions, like where to park the car and what entrance to go into the hospital.

As we made it to through the hospital entrance, we only had the social worker's name. Upon asking where we could find the social worker at the information desk, up came a woman stating, "that is me." I think with all the emotion of the first phone call, my husband forgot that he was told the social worker would meet us in the lobby.

We were escorted to his daughter's room in the mother/baby unit of the hospital. As he saw her, his eyes filled with tears. I stood back and let them just see each other and say the first words. He said, "I am so glad to see you." She said, "Hi Dad, you were the only person I thought I could count on." There was a long silence, and later my husband admitted to me, he really didn't know what to say to her.

Thank goodness for the social worker, who helped us continue the conversation. The social worker asked his daughter if she wanted to tell him why social work was involved during their visit. His daughter cleared her throat and said, "Yes and I am glad you are here to help me through this," looking back at the social worker. "Dad, I have been using drugs and the baby is in the NICU (neonatal intensive care unit), in withdrawal". She continued, "DSS is involved and they are not letting me take the baby, because I don't have a home and need to get treatment."

Now, I understood why the social worker and the Department of Social Services were involved. His daughter had used drugs during pregnancy and needed treatment. The baby was in the NICU and was withdrawing from the drugs that her mother took in pregnancy.

I still was silent. Drugs? No-one in my family ever misused drugs that I knew of, so I had no experience. What do I say? How can I help? I was at a loss and wish I hadn't been in the room right then meeting her for the first time. Then suddenly my husband realized he had not introduced me. At that moment, he turned to me and motioned for me to come forward. He said to his daughter, "You have not met my wife," and introductions were completed.

His daughter said, "we can go up and see the baby." Of course, that was the next thing to do. We all went to the NICU to see the baby. The baby girl looked so small in that incubator. The nurse came by and asked permission to speak about the baby with us present, and his daughter said, "Go ahead, I have nothing to hide anymore."

We then learned more about how the baby was being given drugs to help her control her withdrawal symptoms. We learned the baby was doing well on the drugs. We didn't stay long with the baby. The next stop after his daughter was returned to her hospital room was to accompany the social worker and the DSS worker into a small meeting room. It was there the first hint of our future involvement was revealed. The social worker explained that his daughter had identified my husband as someone who could take care of the baby, while she went into treatment. They called it "kinship placement."

My husband was so emotional about seeing his daughter and meeting his granddaughter, those words of placement didn't sink in at the time. I, however, heard them load and clear and realized our lives were about to change. Our plans for retirement were going away. How are we going to care for a baby? I had to pull myself together and stop those thoughts for the time being. I just had to think about my husband right then and his needs.

The social worker acknowledged that she knew this was a shock and that we were about to receive much information at one time that we would need to think about, discuss with each other and make decisions. I was glad she recognized our shock. The DSS worker told us the many procedures that would follow to make us the "kinship placement." We had to have home visits, come to the hospital and learn how to care for the baby and do much paperwork, to name a few things. I was glad to know the process, and they both answered all our questions. We didn't have many rights then, because we both were still in shock. But after the initial shock, we had many questions that followed over the next few weeks and months.

I don't think either of us ever even considered not taking the baby to care for her. That wasn't ever a question for us. The ride home from the hospital was as silent as the ride to the hospital. Once home, we both got settled, putting away our coats and going on as if nothing happened. Now, I think that was because there was so much noise in our own heads about what this means for us as individuals and as a couple. Then later, my husband and I were in the kitchen, and the silence was broken with a hug. Our first words to each other were that we would care for the baby.

We began making lists and lists of lists that contained supplies, who to tell, how to arrange work, the schedule of hospital visits, and contacts from the hospital. We buried ourselves in the tasks of getting ready to bring this baby to our home.

One thing we missed in all of the preparation was the discussion of how our life was about to change. We were busy with the tasks and shelved the emotions for now. Daily, I went to the hospital to spend time with our new grandbaby. I fell in love, as any grandmother would holding her grandbaby. The nurses taught me how to care for the baby. They taught us the signs of withdrawal and how to look for them. They taught us how to give the baby her medicine. We were told we would have a home health nurse visit us once we got home with the baby. There would be many appointments with the pediatrician, developmental services, home health nurse and the department of social services case worker ,to name a few.

We both had to take a leave of absence from work. Both our employers were understanding, but there was a time limit. We worried if that time would be enough for us to arrange the care for the baby, when we needed to return to work. How would we make all these appointments? Who could we trust enough to care for the baby? The lists never ended of what we needed to do and plan. Those lists replaced the plans we had made when we got married.

The day came to bring the baby home. I was as excited as when I brought my own babies home many years ago. But I had new things to learn. I also felt my age was so apparent. I watched as the young couples were wheeled out of the hospital all new and fresh holding their new baby. Then the wheelchair came for me to be rolled to the front of the hospital holding the baby. At this point in my life, I thought a wheelchair would be used for some other purpose, never to carry me holding a new baby to take home.

Caring for the Newborn

A baby going through withdrawal can be hard to console. We had to learn how to hold her, swaddle her and mostly be patient. Our house was usually quiet, so we knew we could maintain what we had been advised to do by the nurses to keep a calm, quiet environment. Night feedings didn't seem to be a problem, because at our age you seldom sleep a night completely through anyway. But we were tired despite that advantage.

The home health nurse visited a couple times the first week and I looked forward to her visits. She always gave us the reassurance we needed that we were doing a good job and most importantly the baby was doing well. The baby was doing well eating, sleeping, filling diapers and at two months began a little smile, which melted our hearts. We were able to follow the weaning guideline for the methadone she was on to help her with withdrawal symptoms.

We dealt with bouts of diaper rash and stomach upset on occasion. With the help of the nurse and our pediatrician, we seemed to make it through those challenges. The developmental home visits started about the time the nurse visits slowed and that was great to see how this baby girl was moving through her growth. We had to learn special massages, because her hands and arms would get tight.

Working around these schedules required my husband and I to coordinate schedules and eventually beg employers for understanding. Pretty hard for our group of friends, church members and fellow employees to wrap their head around us being new parents.

The Reality of Addiction

My husband's daughter left the hospital and went immediately into a rehabilitation center nearby. I was told over and over how fortunate it was that there was a bed available for her at just the right time. We would take the baby to see her, remembering that we were just a temporary placement. In the rehabilitation center, my step-daughter was able to detoxify from the street drugs. We learned that she had been on multiple drugs. She was started on medically-assisted therapy with Methadone to help her control the urges to use street drugs. Her days were filled with meetings and counseling. At that time, we really thought this was going to be fine, and we would only have the baby for the time she was in the rehabilitation center.

Neither of us understood addiction very well at the beginning of this journey, and so we treated this arrangement as temporary. We were just grandparents caring for our daughter's baby. Addiction wasn't that simple. I have learned so much over the past few years. Multiple times we could not find the baby's mother after she got discharged from rehabilitation. She was arrested a couple times for selling drugs. She was in and out of treatment. That is a full story that she would have to tell.

In the meantime, we transitioned from being grandparents to parents for the baby, then toddler and now soon to be preschooler. We have been the steady caregivers for this little girl, since just after her birth. We love her.

I was the oldest daycare mom by far. My worry now is how society will treat this little girl. It is an obvious question when others see us at school, church, or the store, anywhere, "they can't be the parents, so what is the story there?" The problem with that question is our little girl is left with the stigma that she was born to a mother who used drugs. Does the world think that makes her less of anything? Does it make her less smart? Does it make her an addict someday? Will she always be waiting for her mother to come back? Am I her mother in her mind or in others mind? She is my youngest daughter in my mind and heart. What would happen at this point if her mother did return and want her daughter back? I am haunted by that thought.

My husband still has his daughter in his heart, and it is even less clear for him. Unexpected parenthood is a life we have come to accept and love. We pray every day for her mother's recovery. We try not to think of the mother any different that we think of her baby daughter. That is a big challenge for me and a thought that I remind myself daily. We just don't know where she is today. I hope we both remain healthy to give our little girl her whole childhood with us.

REFLECTIONS

1.   The story is of an unexpected motherhood by a woman who had planned her retirement years with a new husband. The great change for her was becoming a mother to a baby born to her new husband's daughter, whom she had never met. To further complicate the change was learning about addiction and the instability of recovery. The older couple took on the role of parents to the baby that was just supposed to be a temporary placement. They committed themselves to this baby and now little girl and have expressed great love for her.

2.   The current worry for them is how society will treat this little girl they are raising. Will she be affected by stigma from society? Will she have disadvantages due to her history of substance exposure? Will she grow up with uncertainty of who will care for her in the future if her mother returns or her grandparents become ill?

3.   How do we treat families in this situation? Do we make judgements about them? What would be a better response to support them? How can we remove the stigma for this growing little girl?

CHAPTER 10

Indifference and Realization

Retold by Elizabeth Johnson and Jennifer Rumsey

A story of indifferent parenting, substance use and realizations to find a different way to live with addiction and recovery

The Beginning of My Story

My story starts when I was a teenager. I began simply with marijuana. It was never a problem; I really only used on the weekends. Then, after a visit to the doctor for something so insignificant that I cannot even recall, I was prescribed hydrocodone. I didn't know what it was or what it did. When a doctor gave me a medicine, why wouldn't I trust their judgement? I took the medicine as recommended, and I got high. That feeling was one that I wanted to continue, so I started pretending I had ailments. In reality, I was completely healthy.

At first, it was mainly Percocet and Vicodin, with continued marijuana use. I was a teenager, using pain pills that I didn't even understand, but I just liked how they felt. I wonder, had the doctor not prescribed these pills, would I have just found them some other way? Maybe, I would never have found them at all. Maybe, my drug use would have started and ended with marijuana.

Indifference

Being able to hang out with the older kids and my parents' leaving me alone so long as I didn't get in trouble, spelled out disaster. They looked the other way; I didn't have to answer to their authority. I was an adult as a teenager, and my choices were my own. What I did behind my parents' back was my decision, and they just never seemed to care. Everything I did was in their peripheral (not completely in their line of sight), but still impossible to ignore. At the time, their indifference seemed freeing, and I created many bad habits very early. While my habits did not seem serious, if my parents would have disciplined me, I might've stopped those bad tendencies as soon as they started.

Pregnant, Parenting and Escalating Use

As a late teenager, I got pregnant by my boyfriend, and I stopped using any drugs. It really was just that easy. Fortunately, I had my first child with no complications.

After the baby, my boyfriend and I used cocaine and pills a lot. It wasn't out of control, though, but it was still a bad habit to keep. The routine of using pills continued even as my first child was a toddler. But, eventually, after many years of using, hydrocodone just wasn't enough. I sought out other, stronger drugs, like Roxy's (Roxicodone), Dilaudid, and morphine. After ultimately procuring these, I would either snort them or simply swallow the pills.

Thus, began the pattern for the next two years. I could still hold a job, and raise my child, but I was snorting or taking pills constantly. It seemed as though, if I was able to maintain my obligations, then the habit must not be that bad. In truth, I was addicted.

My dependence escalated when I started shooting up the pills. I toppled over the illusionary precipice of control. I was no longer in charge of my own wants and needs. Every action I took or thoughts I had, related to scoring more drugs. My routines were shaken. I was late to everything, including work, school, or anything. My main focus was just on my dependence. I didn't even notice my autonomy slipping through my fingers.It didn't help that my boyfriend was using and selling drugs himself. We lived with my parents and they were indifferent. They often left us alone.

80

A Realization

Eventually, my boyfriend came to the realization that he could not live this way and made the decision to move back in with his parents, several states away. With that epiphany, he left and took our child, as I stayed back.

I continued to shoot up heavy pain pills. I stayed with my family for a whole year before finally deciding to join him. I hoped that this decision would trigger a change in my habits as well. I hoped that moving to a different place would mean I wouldn't have the connections to score drugs that I did here. So, I got on a bus and detoxed the whole way. It was a long bus ride, and the next three days were rough. Pill withdrawal was the worst havoc inflicted on my body that I ever had experienced. To this day, I have not forgotten the way pill withdrawal feels.

Shifting Use

In a way, coming to live with my boyfriend did stop my pill addiction. But, instead, my drug of choice simply shifted. I found methamphetamines, and I started shooting up meth. It was much cheaper than the pills and was all I could find until heroin. When I started using heroin, I knew it would be just like the pills, and stopping would be next to impossible. Thus, I wouldn't shoot up the heroin multiple days in a row, and I told myself I would never get hooked on pills again. These self-imposed ultimatums were my semblance of control. So, even though I still shot up heroin and wanted to do it every day, it did not seem to me as bad as the pills once were. For me, this conviction that heroin seemed better than the pills justified my continued use of the drug. In the midst of all this, and even after being clean for some time, my boyfriend started using again, too.

Baby Two

I soon realized that I was pregnant again. After going to the doctor, it turned out that I had been pregnant for three months without knowing. Even after finding out that I was pregnant, I still used for about a month. It wasn't until five months before the baby was due that I stopped. Fortunately, my baby was normal. After leaving the hospital, I just continued my past habits. I would get babysitters or even bring the baby with me when I did drugs.

In some respects, I was still semi-functioning, but the expenses of my habit were large, and I lost my car. We had to move in with my children's grandmother in order to afford my habit. This life continued for two years, and it almost seemed as though I had improved. While living with my children's grandmother and lacking a car, there just was not as much opportunity to use. I wasn't clean by any means, but I also wasn't using every day. It almost seemed like I was better.

The Illusion

This illusion of recovery was uprooted as soon as we got our own house and a car again. Everything picked up right where it left off. Some changes, it seems, are not for the best. The same habits that caused me to lose my car and my house in the first place resurfaced. But I kept my house and my car, and it seemed as though I could have it all. Eventually, someone called child protective services and displaced my whole system.

Child Protective Services [CPS] determined that my children needed placement for safety reasons. This was somewhat of a wakeup call, because clearly my habits were no longer just affecting me. I could pretend that I was fine. I knew my children were being taken care of, and, even though I didn't want them taken away completely, I just could not pass the CPS drug tests. Up until this point, there was little to no intervention that influenced my habits. I really didn't want my kids to be gone. I didn't want to, but I still used every day.

Breaking the Cycle

I found out I was pregnant again, but even this realization did not curb my habits. I used for 31 out of 37 weeks of my pregnancy. I did not have my other two children with me, while I was pregnant for the third time and still using drugs. When the time came to have this child, I was about to lose my other two children due to these habits. I finally told myself that enough was enough. I decided to seek treatment. I reached out for help, partly because I just did not know if my baby was going to be ok after using for so many weeks of the pregnancy. If I wanted to keep my children and have a healthy baby, I knew that I needed a doctor and help.

Looking back on it, I believe I used for so long during this pregnancy because of the stress of my personal life. My long-term boyfriend (the father of my first two children) and I split up. Although we had split up as a couple, we were still living in the same house. Being pregnant by someone else while living in the same house as my ex-boyfriend was incredibly stressful. The situation just led to me to use even more frequently. My ex-boyfriend and I were constantly fighting. There was a lot of drama, so it was hard to stop using during that time.

I just felt so alone. I knew that I was the only person who would support and care for the baby after it was born, and that was an isolating feeling. I was the only person who would be there to guide the baby growing within me. I knew my baby deserved a mother who cared. Finally, these realizations culminated in my decision to seek help so that my baby and I could be healthy.

A New Start

Eventually, I found a place to receive treatment that would let me keep my child with me. My other two children were with their aunt. Because I had no drugs in my system when my baby was born, she was allowed to stay with me. I've been here for six months now, and I have not used anything.

It has been really hard rebuilding the relationships with people who I let down in my years. They can see a genuine change in me, and I hope not to abuse their help ever again. That is all you can do really - just keep trying.

Reflecting on Why

Reflecting back on my experiences and why my life got to the point where I was abusing substances, I think there were definitely some key moments that could have changed the outcome. From the beginning, my parents' inactive parenting was a disservice to creating the early habits that eventually led to where I am today. They genuinely did not seem to interfere with what I did and the people with whom I associated. Now, I try to be the active parent that mine were not. I feel like, maybe, if someone had been there to stop me in the beginning, it might not have gotten that bad or maybe never happened.

REFLECTIONS

1.   This is the story of a mother who felt alone from the start. She did not have the parental guidance to help her make the right decisions in the beginning. Her habits developed early and grew. The autonomy she was given as a child and teenager resulted in her access and development of bad habits. How do we support parents to understand guidance of children to prevent substance use? Will this mother be an active parent in her children's lives unlike her perception of the way she was raised? How can we support her to develop parental skills?

2.   She found herself pregnant with her third child and feeling utterly lost and alone. She reached a turning point in her life and knew she needed to make a change. She sought help and had a third healthy baby and was even permitted to keep her first two. This story shows the resiliency of a mother and the ability for her to change after an epiphany about the state of her dependency on drugs and losing her children. Why did it take her so long to seek treatment? Where could there have been people offering her support and helping her find recovery in her story?

3.   How can mothers with substance use disorder keep their children after they are in recovery? What kind of long term support and follow-up is available for mothers? How should we make treatment more available for mothers like the one in the story?

CHAPTER 11

The Family I Never Knew I Had

Retold by: Emily Shores and Rebekah Lannamann

The Story of the Significance of my Surroundings

How It All Began

My story starts back at an age that startles many parents. I was 12 when my drug use began. I was 14 by the time I had a miscarriage. That miscarriage was my final push into harder drug use beyond just smoking weed and drinking. I was in an abusive relationship not long after, with a man that is now serving over 10 years in prison. Before my 18th birthday I was in foster care and managed to do my first year sober since I had started using. On my one-year sober date, I relapsed.

The day I became legal and gained freedom, I went wild. I had a car and I had money; nothing was going to hold me back. A year later I was in jail with over 30 charges to my name. I did my second almost-full year sober while on my parole, but it didn't last. My boyfriend was not supportive of my sobriety. When he realized I just wanted to get high, he helped me. We sunk back into addiction together. My next criminal charge was for driving while under the influence. I should not have survived some of the drives I took when I was using. At the time, I worked at a place that allowed us to drink as we cleaned up work. I hung out with a bad crowd; our addictions fed into each other's addictions.

When my boyfriend got out of jail, we settled in together. He wanted to stay clean this time, but I didn't. I drug him back down with me. We both were using again like nothing had changed. I never led myself to a sober environment, and I kept falling back into my old ways.

Carrying My Little Girl

I was five weeks along when I found out I was pregnant. My boyfriend had the option to straighten up with me or get out of my life- I was going to get sober for my future child. Time passed and neither of us followed through on our promise to get clean for the baby. I was using while she was inside me. My boyfriend and I eventually lost our property. He moved back in with his uncle who used, and did things I never imagined he would have done. He went back to jail for that and so many more charges. To get off my meth and pain pill dependency I went on Subutex: the "maintenance med" as a lot of people call it. It is meant to help wean a person off of opioid addiction. One of my best friends was the first person to take me to a clinic and he even paid for my first few visits. Eventually, unable to beat his addiction, my best friend overdosed and died.

After his death, I felt an even stronger need for change in my life. I decided to put in for a referral to a sober home and finally got in after a month of waiting. Unfortunately, the set-up did not work for me and I had to leave shortly after starting my journey to sobriety. I wanted to stay sober.

Bringing Her to Life

My labor was hard. I spent 43.5 hours giving birth. I hemorrhaged. I was low on blood and iron. My baby girl was born 7.3 oz with fluid in her lungs. She spent five days in the Neonatal Intensive Care Unit. I cannot explain how grateful I am that she was there because of her lung issue, and not because she was born addicted to anything. My baby was born free of addiction, even of dependence on Subutex. Despite her low birth weight and other problems, she was overall okay.

Her Finnegan score was only high once. This score assesses common neonatal drug withdrawal symptoms. The higher the score, the greater the chance an infant is having withdrawal. We believe the only time her score was high was because she didn't have enough to eat and didn't sleep well that night; it was close to a 10 then. Most of her scores were around two to three, and the highest one can score is somewhere around 20. We never had to put her on medicine for withdrawal. It was never even discussed. I am so lucky.

He Wants to be a Good Father

My boyfriend wanted and still wants to be a good father. He has made the efforts. He came with me to some doctor's appointments before she was born. He tried his best to be involved. I wanted to give him a chance because he seemed to care a lot about her. He went to jail the week before I had her and was looking at 15 to 20 years. There's a recovery program he could get in to instead of spending those years behind bars; I really hope the judge lets him in. He met our daughter for the first time when he was in prison, so I know he was sober at least for that. He is smart and was great at school, despite the fact he dropped out. I never really was that good at school, so I hope she gets that gene from him.

My boyfriend doesn't like going to meetings or anything like that. Be it Alcoholics Anonymous or Narcotics Anonymous, he will not want to go. I feel like I put my relationship above my pregnancy, and not necessarily just because I wanted her to have a dad. I wish I hadn't been so caught up in everything. Sometimes I worry if anything that may go wrong with my girl is my fault. I wanted to give him the chance to be her dad. I wish that I would've cared more about her safety than trying to salvage the relationship with her father.

The Family I Didn't Know I Had

I never thought my family would want me around again. I didn't know that I would have family in the way I did once my daughter was born. They have been supportive beyond my wildest dreams. I realize that they would have been there all along with open arms, had I just been making the right efforts toward the right things. I didn't know how to even reach out for help, I was so caught up in everything else.

My sister was kind enough to step in and help me. I struggled greatly with my milk supply throughout the early weeks of my baby's life. I believe both my previous drug involvement and my low consumption of fluids played a role in this. My sister has an infant as well and she shared her breastmilk with me. My grandmother even helped when my little girl got sick for a few days. I never knew how much love surrounded me until I got out of the substance abuse and saw clearly for the first time.

My sober living program keeps me really busy during the day, so it was nice to have family to depend on for a little. Now my girl has started day care. It's scary, but I am working on letting others take care of her. I can pump and send her with my own milk since I can make enough now.

The Change Sobriety Brought Me

When you're sober, you actually worry about things. Doctor's appointments and dentist visits are suddenly at the front of your mind; the stuff that didn't matter before, now matters. I worry about what my past substance abuse may have done to my brain. I worry about my girl's development. Did my Subutex treatments potentially impact her while I carried her? There's not much research on what happens to children that come from a mom who had a dependence on Subutex. I guess I will just have to watch and see as she grows. She's been meeting her milestones, but they're all just physical right now. I worry about her mental development down the road because of my actions.

Addiction is addiction. You can almost feel stuck in it sometimes but that doesn't make you a bad person, it just makes you a sick person. The best way to get unstuck is seeking treatment and really listening to the higher power concept. That's the only way I got sober and the only way I stay sober is God and my meetings. Being in treatment is really important for me too. Learning about addiction in classes or inpatient or whatever way. It doesn't matter how you learn just that you do learn. You realize that everybody thinks about things differently. I can take what I learned and apply it to myself and understand my habits and how to fight them. It lets me catch myself before falling back into the same thing. It doesn't make you a bad person just because you can't quit.

For me, a lot of it is about my relationship with God; it's a spiritual relationship. It isn't about trying to be religious and perfect and doing everything just right. It's about having a spiritual relationship with a higher power because that is the only thing that fills the void that addiction left me. I let my craving be for him, and not for substance.

The definition of insanity is doing the same thing over and over again but expecting different results. The same people, places, and things mean you're going to do the same old stuff when it comes to addiction. You have to get away from the place and the people and start over if you want it all to stop. I did and now I'm doing so well for my little girl.

Once you get sober you can think straight and clearly. Now I make sober, rational, normal decisions and it is so much easier to stay that way. Things matter how they should. I get to experience emotions for what they really are, in a way I never did before when I was abusing substances.

REFLECTIONS

1.   How It All Began.
       How can education in the school system help to prevent these
       types of things from happening? How can foster care be improved so
       that these children are taught better?

2.   Carrying My Little Girl
       How can programs be implemented for women like this one in
       order for them to find people who truly care about what they
       are going through. What types of assumptions do people
       make about pregnant women who are struggling with addiction that
       can potentially cause more harm and shame for the women who are
       struggling?

3.   Bringing Her to Life
       The mother notes ample knowledge on the testing/scoring that
       her baby received while in the NICU, how can more knowledge and
       awareness of the baby's health affect the mother's efforts to become
       sober?

4.   He Wants to be a Good Father
       How can dependence on the wrong type of people be detrimental
       to the success of a recovery program?

5.   The Family I Didn't Know I Had
       How can dependency on other people affect~both positively and
       negatively~the outcome of a struggling addict's pathway to sobriety?
       How can business or work be beneficial to the success of a sober
       ing addict?

6.   The Change Sobriety Brought Me
       Discuss ways in which current addicts can be influenced by how
       women like this mother are able to see the world in a different way
       after becoming sober.

CHAPTER 12

Resources

Mother to Baby
https://mothertobaby.org/
Call: 866-626-6847
Text: 855-999-3525
e-mail: contactus@mothertobaby.org
Questions to experts about any substance use during pregnancy or breast-feeding including medications, alcohol, herbs and more as to risks to mother and infant based on current research.

National Institute on Drug Abuse
https://www.drugabuse.gov/publications/principles-drug-addiction-treatment-research-based-guide-third-edition/resources

The Substance Abuse and Mental Health Services Administration
https://www.addictionguide.com/resources/

For Local resources contact your Local United Way Help Line

Mothers with Addicted Children - Hazelden Betty Ford
https://www.hazeldenbettyford.org/resources-for/mothers-addicted-children

Made in the USA
Monee, IL
25 January 2022

89782056R00066